STARS

Strategies
To
Achieve
Reading
Success

D1284129

Curriculum Associates

ACKNOWLEDGMENTS

Product Development

Developers and Authors: Deborah Adcock, Joan Krensky

Contributing Writers: Patricia Delanie, Laura Johnson, Jo Pitkin

Editorial Project Managers

Deborah Adcock, Pamela Seastrand

Design

Cover Designer: Matt Pollock

Book Designer: Pat Lucas

Illustration/Photography Credits

iStockphoto LP/front cover, title page

Jamie Ruh/page 6

Pat Lucas/page 8

Susan Hawk/pages 10, 13, 27, 30, 36, 60, 89, 120, 122, 130, 134, 136, 143

©JupiterImages Corporation/pages 16, 21, 28, 40, 42, 46, 50, 55, 67, 74, 81, 84, 86, 96, 104, 110, 113, 132

Jim Roldan/pages 18, 45, 62, 76, 140

Courtesy of U.S. Fish and Wildlife Service/page 22

Library of Congress, LC-USZ62-7816/page 31

Courtesy of McDonald's Corporation/page 33

Hillary Crosman/page 34

Courtesy of Jerry Search/Southern California Speed Skating Association/page 56

Mary Newell DePalma/page 68

Chuck Aghoian/Shutterstock.com/page 70

Micheal Shake/Shutterstock.com/page 70

Gary Torrisi/page 108

International Landmarks/Corel/page 124

Portrait Gallery/Perry-Castañeda Library, University of Texas at Austin/pages 128 and 146

TABLE OF CONTENTS

FINDING MAIN IDEA

What Is Main Idea?

Books, short stories, and poems all tell a story. All stories have a main idea. A movie or television show also tells a story that has a main idea. The main idea tells what something is mostly about.

1 Write the name of a movie you enjoyed watching.

_____

2 Write three important things that happened in the movie.

_____

_____

_____

3 Write a sentence that tells what the movie was mostly about.

_____

_____

_____

 Work with a Partner

- Tell your partner about a book or newspaper article you have read.
- Then take turns telling about the main idea of the book or article. Tell your main idea in one sentence.

How Do You Find the Main Idea?

You can find the main idea of most reading passages in the first or last sentence of the passage.

Read this passage about sandhill cranes. Think about the most important idea in the passage.

> Sandhill cranes in northern Canada migrate to warmer climates in the fall. The birds fly thousands of miles during their travels. Many sandhill cranes travel to the Gulf Coast of the United States. Some travel as far south as Mexico.

1. Let's look at the chart below.

    The sentences in the top three boxes tell about the main idea of the passage, but they do not tell the most important idea.

2. Look again at the passage. The first sentence in the passage does tell the most important idea. This sentence tells what the passage is mostly about.

3. Write this main idea in the empty box below.

The birds fly thousands of miles during their travels.	Many sandhill cranes travel to the Gulf Coast of the United States.	Some travel as far south as Mexico.

WHAT TO KNOW

The most important idea in a paragraph is called the **main idea**. The main idea tells what a paragraph is mostly about.

- The main idea is sometimes found in the first sentence of a paragraph.
- The main idea is sometimes found in the last sentence of a paragraph.
- The main idea is sometimes not found in any one sentence. You can figure out the main idea by asking yourself, "What is the most important idea in the paragraph?"

Read this paragraph about bats. As you read, think about the most important idea in the paragraph.

Why Bats Can Fly in the Dark

Sometimes, people say that someone who doesn't see well is "as blind as a bat." Bats are not really blind, however. Most of them have tiny eyes that cannot see very well in the dark. So bats rely on their ears to "see" at night. Bats make high squeaking noises as they fly. These sounds spread out through the air like waves. When the sounds hit an object, they bounce back as echoes. The bats' large ears easily pick up the echo sounds to locate objects in their path. This is called echolocation. Bats use echolocation to hunt and to avoid bumping into things in the dark.

A bat sends out sounds through the air waves.

The last sentence of the paragraph states the most important idea.

Bats use echolocation to hunt and to avoid bumping into things in the dark.

Read this e-mail that a girl sent to her friend. As you read, think about the main idea of the e-mail. Then answer the questions.

From: Robin S. <RobinS@lion.xyz>   To: Tamara H. <TamaraH@lion.xyz>
Subject: Interesting facts of the day

Tamara,

I want to tell you about some interesting facts I learned today about geography in the United States. Do you know which state lies the farthest south? Most of the kids in my class answered "Florida." A few kids said "Texas." My response was "California." We were all wrong! The most southern state is Hawaii. We also learned that Alaska is both the most western and the most eastern state. Its Aleutian Islands extend really far to the west. They actually cross the line that divides the Eastern and Western hemispheres. Another interesting fact I learned is that parts of Virginia are farther west than West Virginia. Also, did you know that parts of Wisconsin, which is in the Midwest, are farther east than parts of Florida?

Reply soon,
Robin

1. What is the main idea of the paragraph?
   Ⓐ The state that lies farthest south is Hawaii.
   Ⓑ Robin's entire class answered a geography question incorrectly.
   Ⓒ Robin learned some interesting facts about United States geography.
   Ⓓ Parts of Wisconsin are farther east than parts of Florida.

2. Where or how did you find the main idea?
   Ⓐ in the first sentence of the paragraph
   Ⓑ in the last sentence of the paragraph
   Ⓒ in the middle of the paragraph
   Ⓓ by thinking about the most important idea in the paragraph

Work with a Partner

- Talk about your answers to the questions.
- Tell why you chose your answers.
- Then talk about what you have learned so far about finding main idea.

REVIEW

The main idea tells what a paragraph is mostly about.

- Read the first sentence of the paragraph.
  The main idea is sometimes found here.

- Read the last sentence of the paragraph.
  The main idea is sometimes found here.

- Sometimes, the main idea is not found in a sentence
  from the paragraph. You can figure out the main idea by
  thinking about the most important idea in the paragraph.

Read this fable by Aesop. As you read, ask yourself, "What is the fable mostly about?" Then answer the questions.

A jay ventured into a yard where peacocks often gathered to eat corn. There, on the ground, the jay found several colorful peacock feathers. Because he greatly admired peacocks, the jay tied the feathers to his own tail and strutted toward a group of peacocks. The peacocks were quite angry at the jay for pretending to be one of them. They plucked the borrowed feathers off his tail. The jay walked back to some other jays that had watched the ugly scene. They, too, were angry. They told him, "It is not only fine feathers that make fine birds."

3. What is the fable mostly about?
    Ⓐ what peacocks eat
    Ⓑ how birds can change their feathers
    Ⓒ the difference between different
        kinds of bird feathers
    Ⓓ a bird that pretends to be
        a different kind of bird

4. Where or how did you find the main idea?
    Ⓐ in the first sentence of the paragraph
    Ⓑ in the last sentence of the paragraph
    Ⓒ in the middle of the paragraph
    Ⓓ by thinking about the most important
        idea in the paragraph.

Which Answer Is Correct and Why?

**Look at the answer choices for each question.
Read why each answer choice is correct or not correct.**

3. **What is the fable mostly about?**

   Ⓐ **what peacocks eat**

   This answer is not correct because while the fable does state that peacocks eat corn, it is only a detail. It is not the most important idea.

   Ⓑ **how birds can change their feathers**

   This answer is not correct because the way that the jay tried to change his feathers is only a detail in the story. The way he attempted to change his feathers is not the most important idea.

   Ⓒ **the difference between different kinds of bird feathers**

   This answer is not correct because there is not enough information in the fable to support this idea. While the fable does suggest that peacock feathers are more beautiful than jay feathers, it is not the most important idea.

   ⬤ **a bird that pretends to be a different kind of bird**

   This answer is correct because it explains the lesson that is taught in the fable. It tells what all the sentences in the fable are mostly about. It is the most important idea.

4. **Where did you find the main idea?**

   Ⓐ **in the first sentence of the paragraph**

   This answer is not correct because the first sentence in the fable tells about the setting. It states that the jay was going into the yard where peacocks often gathered. This is not the most important idea of the paragraph.

   ⬤ **in the last sentence of the paragraph**

   This answer is correct because the last sentence states, *"It is not only fine feathers that make fine birds."* The idea that fine appearances are not the most important part of being a fine bird is the lesson and main idea of the fable.

   Ⓒ **in the middle of the paragraph**

   This answer is not correct because the sentences in the middle of the paragraph tell about how the jay tied peacock feathers to his own tail and how the peacocks and jays reacted to what he had done.

   Ⓓ **by thinking about the most important idea in the paragraph**

   This answer is not correct because the main idea is stated in the last sentence.

MORE TO KNOW

- Each paragraph in a reading passage has one main idea. The entire reading passage also has one main idea. The main idea of an entire reading passage is often found in the first or last paragraph.
- The title of a reading passage often helps you identify the main idea.

Read this history report about a national symbol. Then answer the questions.

Who Is Uncle Sam?

Uncle Sam has been a symbol of the United States for more than 150 years. The first drawings of Uncle Sam appeared in the 1830s. For many years, his appearance took many forms. By the 1860s, drawings of Uncle Sam became more alike. Most pictures show a tall, thin man with a white beard. He is dressed in a tailcoat, striped pants, and a top hat with a band of stars.

Uncle Sam was actually based on a real person. He was a meat packer from Troy, New York. His name was Samuel Wilson, but everyone called him Uncle Sam. During the War of 1812, Wilson supplied meat to U.S. Army troops stationed near Troy. He stamped the letters U.S. on each wooden barrel of beef and pork. Soldiers thought the initials stood for Uncle Sam. The letters, however, were actually the abbreviation for the United States. Soon, Uncle Sam became the term for anything referring to the United States.

5. What is the main idea of the first paragraph?
   - Ⓐ Uncle Sam has been a U.S. symbol for more than 150 years.
   - Ⓑ Uncle Sam is a tall, thin, bearded man.
   - Ⓒ The first drawings of Uncle Sam appeared in the 1830s.
   - Ⓓ For many years, no one knew what Uncle Sam looked like.

6. What is the main idea of paragraph 2?
   - Ⓐ Uncle Sam was from Troy, New York.
   - Ⓑ Wilson sold meat to the U.S. Army.
   - Ⓒ Uncle Sam was based on a real person.
   - Ⓓ The letters *U.S.* stood for *Uncle Sam.*

7. What is the report mostly about?
   - Ⓐ symbols of the United States
   - Ⓑ one of our nation's oldest symbols
   - Ⓒ what Uncle Sam looked like
   - Ⓓ the real Uncle Sam

8. Which of these is another good title for the report?
   - Ⓐ "Uncle Sam's Costume"
   - Ⓑ "American Symbols"
   - Ⓒ "Uncle Sam Wilson"
   - Ⓓ "The History of Uncle Sam"

Read this article about a special kind of mouse. Then answer the questions.

In 1968, Douglas Engelbart showed off a new device at a computer conference. The gadget was a little wooden box on wheels. It was so small that it fit into the palm of the hand. Many people showed great interest in Engelbart's invention. Sixteen years passed, though, before "the mouse" became a common computer tool.

In the late 1960s, computers were huge machines that cost millions of dollars. The first small computers began to appear during the 1970s. But few people used the early computers at home. Users needed to know special computer languages to operate them.

Personal computers became more popular after 1984. That was the year that Apple Computer, Inc., introduced the Macintosh®. The "Mac" was the first easy-to-use computer. Part of its basic equipment was a mouse. It controlled the movement of a pointer, or cursor, on the screen. The mouse let users point and click to give commands to the computer. The mouse was also an excellent drawing tool. It could be used to form curved and straight lines.

Today, most computers come with a mouse. Some computers have other hand-controlled devices, too. Some of the devices are trackballs, touch pads, and joysticks.

9. What is the main idea of the first paragraph?
   - Ⓐ Early personal computers were hard to operate.
   - Ⓑ The Mac was the first easy-to-use computer.
   - Ⓒ Douglas Engelbart invented the first computer mouse.
   - Ⓓ A computer mouse is a hand-held device.

10. Paragraph 3 is mostly about
   - Ⓐ how the Mac was made.
   - Ⓑ how the Mac made good use of the mouse.
   - Ⓒ how the mouse has changed in design.
   - Ⓓ how to use hand-controlled devices.

11. What is the article mostly about?
   - Ⓐ a device that is as small as a mouse
   - Ⓑ Macintosh computers
   - Ⓒ an invention that changed the way computers were used
   - Ⓓ the work of Douglas Engelbart throughout the years

12. Which of these is the best title for the article?
   - Ⓐ "How the Mouse Came to Be"
   - Ⓑ "The Brave Little Mouse"
   - Ⓒ "A Man with a Vision"
   - Ⓓ "Computer Tools"

TEST TIPS	• A test question about the main idea may ask you what a reading passage is *mostly* or *mainly* about.
	• A test question about the main idea may ask you to choose the best title for a reading passage. A good title often identifies the main idea of the whole reading passage.

Read this poem about someone's home. Then answer questions about the poem. Choose the best answer for Numbers 13 and 14.

Home Is Where the Heart Is
by stevan-adele Morley

Under a mighty mountain,
    at the bottom of a hill,
The valley in the morning
    is so beautiful and still.

Grandfather lives on the mountain;
    my cousin lives on the hill,
But I live deep in the valley
    and believe I always will.

Eagles nest on the mountain;
    birds fly down from the hill,
Bringing songs to the valley
    that echo through the chill.

When the snow melts on the mountain,
    it comes streaming down the hill
To the river in the valley
    that gives power to our mill.

There's folks who love the mountain,
    and folks who love the hill,
But I live deep in the valley
    and believe I always will.

13. The poem is mostly about
  Ⓐ someone's feelings about living in the valley.
  Ⓑ people who like living on a mighty mountain.
  Ⓒ a mill powered by melting snow.
  Ⓓ bird songs that echo through a valley.

14. Another good title for the poem is
  Ⓐ "Songs from Up High."
  Ⓑ "A Mighty Mountain."
  Ⓒ "My Valley Home."
  Ⓓ "Mountain Folk."

Read this passage adapted from a folktale told by the Kutchin Indians of Canada. Then answer questions about the folktale. Choose the best answer for Numbers 15 and 16.

One night, when Fox was hungry, he asked his friend Raven if he had any food.

"I have food in my nest," said Raven, "but I cannot get it for you until morning. Ever since the moon disappeared, it is too dark to fly at night."

Fox sighed. "Ever since the moon disappeared, it's hard for me to hunt at night."

Fox and Raven decided that they had to get the moon back. Bear had stolen the moon because its bright light kept him awake all night.

"But we are small and Bear is so large. If he took the moon, we won't be able to get it back."

"Then we must trick him," said Raven. "I have an idea." The two friends went to Bear's cave.

"Are you home, Bear?" Fox called out. "Your friends Fox and Raven are here to see you."

"Please wait a moment," said Bear. "I have to tidy up my cave so that it looks presentable for guests." After a few minutes, Bear told Fox and Raven to come in. "We have an exciting story to share with you," said Raven.

"I love stories," said Bear. "Please, tell me!"

Raven went on to tell Bear a very long and very dull story. While Raven distracted Bear with the story, Fox searched the cave for the moon.

"This isn't an exciting story at all," said Bear, yawning. His eyes were growing heavy.

"Be patient, Bear," said Raven. "The best part is coming."

Raven continued telling his story, but Bear was so bored that he fell asleep. Fox emerged with a bag he had found under Bear's bed. In the bag was the moon.

Fox and Raven ran out of the cave with the moon, but Bear woke up and began chasing them. Fox and Raven threw the moon back into the sky.

Bear was angry. "How am I supposed to sleep now?"

"Raven needs the light of the moon to fly at night," explained Fox, "and I need it to hunt. So, on nights when we have eaten early and retired to our homes, you may pull the moon from the sky and sleep in the darkness."

And so, that is why the moonlight is bright in the sky on some nights while on others it is not.

15. What is the folktale mostly about?
- Ⓐ why Bear preferred darkness
- Ⓑ why the moon appears in the sky only on some nights
- Ⓒ how the moon was taken away from Bear
- Ⓓ who is responsible for the moonlight

16. What is the best title for the folktale?
- Ⓐ "A Moon for Bear"
- Ⓑ "Sail On, Moon"
- Ⓒ "The Hungry Animals"
- Ⓓ "The Stolen Moon"

What Are Facts and Details?

Everything you read contains facts and details. A television show also contains facts and details. The facts and details of the television show tell more about the main idea.

1 Write the main idea of a television show you watched in the past few days.

_____

_____

_____

2 Write three important things that tell more about the main idea of the show.

_____

_____

_____

_____

_____

_____

 Work with a Partner

- Tell your partner about a story you read or a favorite movie.
- Take turns telling about the setting of the story or movie. Tell all the facts and details that describe the setting.
- When you are done, choose one word to describe the place where the story or movie takes place.

How Do You Find Facts and Details?

You can find the facts and details in a reading passage by thinking about the main idea. Once you know the main idea, you can find the details that tell more about the main idea.

Read this passage about Jared. Think about what it is mostly about.

> Jared was very excited when he came to school today. He could barely sit still in class. At lunch, Jared finally told his friends why he couldn't stop smiling. <u>Jared's mother was going to have a baby</u>.

1. First, let's find the main idea of the passage. The main idea is found in the last sentence. It is underlined for you.

2. Next, find the details that tell more about the main idea.

   Look at the chart below. The box at the top tells the main idea.

   The boxes along the bottom show the facts and details that tell more about the main idea.

3. Fill in the detail that is missing from the middle box below.

WHAT TO KNOW

Sentences that tell more about the main idea are called **facts and details**. Facts and details explain or support the most important idea in the paragraph.

- Facts and details provide information about the main idea.
- Facts and details often tell about the *who, what, where, when, why,* and *how* of the main idea.

Read this paragraph about a famous building. The main idea is found in the last sentence and is underlined for you. As you read, think about the sentences that tell more about the main idea.

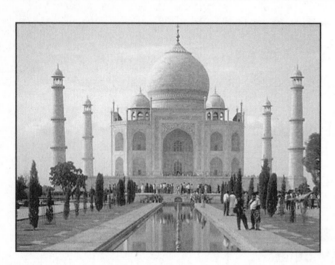

The Taj Mahal is named for Mumtaz Mahal. She was the wife of Indian ruler Shah Jahan. When his beloved wife died, Shah Jahan ordered that a great tomb be built in her memory. Work began on the Taj Mahal in 1632. It took 20,000 workers more than 20 years to complete. The huge, white marble tomb is surrounded by gardens and fountains. A long reflecting pool is set in front of it. <u>The Taj Mahal is India's most famous monument.</u>

The sentences that tell more about the main idea are:

The Taj Mahal is named for Mumtaz Mahal.

She was the wife of Indian ruler Shah Jahan.

When his beloved wife died, Shah Jahan ordered that a great tomb be built in her memory.

Work began on the Taj Mahal in 1632.

It took 20,000 workers more than 20 years to complete.

The huge, white marble tomb is surrounded by gardens and fountains.

A long reflecting pool is set in front of it.

Read this paragraph about the planets. The main idea is found in the first sentence and is underlined for you. As you read, think about the facts and details that tell more about the main idea. Then answer the questions.

Orbiting the Planets

Some of the planets in our solar system have more moons than others. Mercury and Venus, the planets closest to the sun, have no moons. Our planet, Earth, has one moon. Two oddly shaped moons orbit our neighbor Mars. Several planets, though, have many moons. Eight moons revolve around blue Neptune. At least 15 moons orbit Uranus, and at least 16 orbit Jupiter, the largest planet. Saturn, the planet with the largest and most spectacular rings, has the most moons. Scientists have confirmed that at least 18 moons orbit Saturn.

1. Which planet has the most moons?
   Ⓐ Jupiter
   Ⓑ Uranus
   Ⓒ Saturn
   Ⓓ Neptune

2. Which detail tells something about Mars?
   Ⓐ It has at least 15 moons.
   Ⓑ It is closest to the sun.
   Ⓒ Eight moons revolve around it.
   Ⓓ Two oddly shaped moons orbit it.

Work with a Partner

- Talk about your answers to the questions.
- Tell why you chose your answers.
- Then talk about what you have learned so far about recalling facts and details.

REVIEW	Facts and details explain or support the main idea.
	• Look for sentences that provide information about the main idea.
	• Look for sentences that tell about the *who, what, where, when, why,* and *how* of the main idea.

Read this fairy tale by Hans Christian Andersen. As you read, ask yourself, "What is the main idea? What facts and details tell *more* about the main idea?" Then answer the questions.

The Princess and the Pea

There once was a prince who wanted to marry a princess, but she would have to be a real princess. The prince traveled all around the world to find his princess. There were princesses enough, but there was always something about them that was not quite right. So the disappointed prince went home.

One evening, a terrible storm erupted. Thunder boomed and lightning flashed, and rain poured down in torrents. Suddenly, there was a knocking at the city gate. The king himself went to open it and found a princess standing outside. What a sight she was after all that rain! Water streamed from her hair and clothes. Despite her sloppy appearance, she claimed that she was a real princess.

"We will soon find out," thought the doubtful queen. She went into the bedchamber, took all the bedding off the bedstead, and laid a pea at the bottom. Then she took 20 eiderdown mattresses and laid them upon the pea. On this the princess had to lie all night.

In the morning, the princess was asked how she had slept. "Oh, miserably!" she said. "Goodness knows what was in my bed, but I was lying on something hard, and now I am black and blue all over."

Now it was clear that the young woman was a real princess, because nobody but a true princess could be so delicate. So the prince and the princess married, and the pea was put in a museum, where it may still be today.

3. The pea was put under the mattresses by the
   - Ⓐ king.
   - Ⓑ queen.
   - Ⓒ prince.
   - Ⓓ princess.

4. How did the prince feel when he went home without having found a real princess?
   - Ⓐ puzzled
   - Ⓑ angry
   - Ⓒ disappointed
   - Ⓓ doubtful

Which Answer Is Correct and Why?

Look at the answer choices for each question.
Read why each answer choice is correct or not correct.

3. **The pea was put under the mattresses by the**

   Ⓐ **king.**

   This answer is not correct because the only time the king is mentioned in the fairy tale is when he greets the princess at the city gate.

   ⬤ **queen.**

   This answer is correct because paragraph 3 states that the queen laid 20 mattresses upon the pea.

   Ⓒ **prince.**

   This answer is not correct because the fairy tale never mentions that the prince was involved in placing the pea under the mattresses.

   Ⓓ **princess.**

   This answer is not correct because the fairy tale indicates that the princess knew nothing about the pea being put under the mattresses she would sleep upon. When she awoke the next morning, she had no idea why she had slept so badly.

4. **How did the prince feel when he went home without having found a real princess?**

   Ⓐ **puzzled**

   This answer is not correct because the word *puzzled* was not used in the fairy tale to describe the prince.

   Ⓑ **angry**

   This answer is not correct because the fairy tale never states that the prince was angry about anything.

   ⬤ **disappointed**

   This answer is correct because the first paragraph states that, after he failed to find a real princess, "*the disappointed prince went home.*"

   Ⓓ **doubtful**

   This answer is not correct because it was the queen who was doubtful, not the prince. She doubted that the princess who appeared at the gate was a real princess.

MORE TO KNOW	Facts and details give additional meaning to the main idea of a reading passage. When you read, look for sentences that

- describe a person, place, or thing.
- tell the order in which things happen.
- explain how to do something.
- share an experience, idea, or opinion.

Read this message written on the back of a postcard. Then answer the questions.

Dear Freddie,

    Here I am in the Philippines, at last. I haven't done much yet. However, I did see some unusual sights on the drive from the airport to my uncle's home. I spotted these buses called "jeepneys." The owners paint their jeepneys in bold, bright colors. Then they cover them with all kinds of decorations. Jeepneys also have many mirrors—more than are needed for safety!

    My taxi driver told me that the first jeepneys were created from U.S. Army jeeps. The jeeps had been left on the Philippine Islands after World War II. Filipinos made the vehicles longer to hold more passengers. Today, most jeepneys can carry about 17 people comfortably. But many more passengers usually squeeze in.

                           Your friend,
                           Eric

5. The first jeepneys were created from
   - Ⓐ taxis.
   - Ⓑ buses.
   - Ⓒ U.S. Army vehicles.
   - Ⓓ cars made in the Philippines.

6. Which of these is true?
   - Ⓐ The first jeepneys were made during World War II.
   - Ⓑ The U.S. Army uses jeepneys.
   - Ⓒ Jeepneys are noisy.
   - Ⓓ Jeepneys are brightly painted.

7. Where did Eric first see jeepneys?
   - Ⓐ on his uncle's street
   - Ⓑ on the drive to his uncle's home
   - Ⓒ on a U.S. Army base
   - Ⓓ on a bus tour

8. Which detail tells more about the main idea of the last paragraph?
   - Ⓐ Owners like to decorate their jeepneys.
   - Ⓑ Jeepneys often have more mirrors than are needed.
   - Ⓒ Jeepneys are longer than army jeeps.
   - Ⓓ Only 17 people can fit in a jeepney.

Read this article about a popular sport. Then answer the questions.

Today, millions of children and adults play the world's most popular sport—soccer. Pelé, who is probably the sport's greatest player, once called soccer "the beautiful game."

Soccer is played on a field that is between 100 and 130 yards long and 50 and 100 yards wide. A goal net, 8 yards wide and 8 feet high, sits at each end of the field. Each team has 11 players—10 field players and 1 goalkeeper. The object of the game is to move a leather-covered rubber ball down the field by dribbling or passing. When the ball is near the opposing team's goal, players try to shoot it into the net. Players may use their feet, knees, chest, and head to control the ball. Only the goalkeepers may touch the ball with their hands. Each game is divided into halves. The team that scores more goals by the end of the second half wins the game.

Since 1900, soccer teams from various nations have competed in the Summer Olympics, which are held every four years. The true soccer championship, however, is the World Cup soccer tournament. It is also held every four years. More than one billion people worldwide watch the World Cup games.

9. What is one detail that tells about soccer?
   Ⓐ Goal nets are 8 feet wide and 8 feet high.
   Ⓑ Soccer was first played in 1800.
   Ⓒ Only goalkeepers can touch the ball with their hands.
   Ⓓ Over one billion people play on soccer teams around the world.

10. What detail tells about the main idea of paragraph 2?
   Ⓐ Players may use their feet to control the ball.
   Ⓑ A soccer team has 10 players.
   Ⓒ The World Cup is held every four years.
   Ⓓ Millions of people play soccer.

11. Who is Pelé?
   Ⓐ a popular soccer coach
   Ⓑ an Olympic athlete
   Ⓒ a goalkeeper
   Ⓓ a famous soccer player

12. Which of these tells more about the main idea of the last paragraph?
   Ⓐ National soccer teams compete in the Winter Olympics.
   Ⓑ More than one billion people watch the World Cup games.
   Ⓒ The true soccer championship is the Summer Olympics.
   Ⓓ Soccer games are divided into halves.

TEST TIPS	• A test question about facts and details may ask you about something that is stated in a reading passage.
	• A test question about facts and details may ask you about the *who, what, where, when, why,* and *how* of the main idea.

Read this essay that a student wrote after a trip to the zoo. Then answer questions about the essay. Choose the best answer for Numbers 13 and 14.

A Walking Pinecone

Have you ever heard of a pangolin? Before this weekend, I would have guessed that a pangolin was some type of musical instrument. During a visit to the zoo, though, I learned that a pangolin is actually a kind of anteater.

The pangolin lives in Africa and India. The pangolin looks like a giant pinecone with legs. Its body is about three-to-five feet long and covered with large brown scales. The scales are thick and sharp to protect the anteater. The pangolin can also roll up into a tight ball for safety. Once the pangolin is curled up, it's impossible for its enemies to unroll it!

Although its nose is not quite as long as the nose of other anteaters, the pangolin does have a good sense of smell. It uses this sense to find food at night. Pangolins eat mostly ants and termites. These anteaters use the sharp claws on their front limbs to rip open the insects' nests. Then they use their long, sticky tongue to pick up the bugs they find inside. Pangolins don't have teeth for chewing their food, so they swallow small pebbles to help them crush up any insects in their stomach.

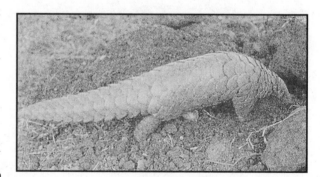

pangolin

13. What is one fact about pangolins?
   Ⓐ They live in Africa only.
   Ⓑ They have a short nose.
   Ⓒ Thick, sharp scales cover their bodies.
   Ⓓ They roll up into a tight ball to sleep.

14. Which part of their body do pangolins use to pick up insects?
   Ⓐ nose
   Ⓑ tongue
   Ⓒ front claws
   Ⓓ teeth

Read this medieval tale from England. Then answer questions about the tale. Choose the best answer for Numbers 15 and 16.

The Boy Merlin

Long ago, a wicked king named Vortigern ruled most of England. Vortigern had many enemies, and eventually he was driven into the mountains of Wales. There, Vortigern tried to build a stone fortress that would protect him from attack. Each day, the king's workers raised the fortress walls, but each night, the rocks tumbled down. Finally, the king called in his wizards to explain the mystery and advise him how to solve it.

"You must find a child born without a human father," they told him. "Slay him, and then the fortress walls will stand firm." So the king sent out a search party to find such a child.

One day, the king's men came upon several children playing ball. One boy threw the ball again and again, but none of the others could catch it. Suddenly, another child shouted out, "You never play fairly, Merlin! You're just a trickster who never had a father!"

The king's men began asking the villagers about the boy. Upon learning that the child's father was not a mortal man, the king's men seized Merlin. Then they rode back to Wales, where Merlin was brought before the king.

"Why have you sent for me?" the young boy demanded. When Vortigern told him the reason, Merlin said, "Your wizards are wrong. By slaying me, you won't keep your fortress standing. There is a pool of water beneath the fortress that is making the ground unsteady. Have your workers dig into the earth until they find the pool. Order them to drain the pool. At the bottom, they will find two stones. Inside the stones are two sleeping dragons."

The king instructed his workers to do as Merlin said. They uncovered the stones, from which two great dragons, one white and one red, burst forth. The dragons began to fight fiercely. At last, the white dragon killed the red one.

"What is the meaning of the dragons' fight?" the frightened king asked.

"The white dragon stands for enemies who will someday slay you," Merlin calmly explained.

Soon afterward, King Vortigern was, indeed, killed by his foes.

15. What material was used to build Vortigern's fortress?
   Ⓐ stones
   Ⓑ wood
   Ⓒ mud
   Ⓓ iron

16. Which of these is a fact from the tale?
   Ⓐ Merlin became one of the king's wizards.
   Ⓑ Merlin told the king that his wizards were wrong.
   Ⓒ Two red dragons lived under the king's fortress.
   Ⓓ Earthquakes caused the fortress walls to tumble down each night.

UNDERSTANDING SEQUENCE

PART ONE: Think About the Strategy

What Is Sequence?

Most things you read are told in order. A science experiment tells what to do first, next, and so on. A nonfiction book usually tells about events in the order in which they happened. Stories have a beginning, a middle, and an ending. Many of the things you do each day are also done in a particular order.

1 Write three things that you did yesterday.

_____

_____

_____

2 List and number these things in the order in which you did them.

_____

_____

_____

 Work with a Partner

- Tell your partner about one of your favorite fiction books.
- Take turns telling about the beginning, the middle, and the ending of the book. Try to use only one sentence to describe each part.

How Do You Find Sequence?

You can find the order in which things happen in an article by thinking about the time order in which things are presented. Writers of articles often introduce information in the order in which events take place.

Read this passage about Ellis Island. Pay attention to the time order of events.

> The government began using Ellis Island in New York Harbor as an immigration station in 1892. The island's use as a major immigration station ended in 1924. The station closed in 1954. In 1965, the island became a national historic site.

1. Let's think about the order in which information is presented in the passage.

2. Look at the time line below.

   The time line tells the order in which events happened in the passage.

3. Fill in the missing information from the passage that tells what event happened in 1954.

1892	1924	1954	1965
The government began using Ellis Island in New York Harbor as an immigration station.	The island's use as a major immigration station ended.	_____ _____ _____	The island became a national historic site.

WHAT TO KNOW

The order in which things are done or events take place is called **sequence**. The steps for completing a set of directions often follow a sequence.

- Clue words such as *first, next, then, last, finally, before,* and *after* often tell you when things are done or events happen.
- Clues such as times of day, days of the week, months, seasons, and years tell when things happen.
- In a story without clue words, think about the beginning, the middle, and the ending to help you figure out sequence. In an article without clue words, think about the order in which things take place or how things are done.

Read this article that describes an art project. As you read, think about the order of the steps to complete the project.

Making a Collage

Ms. Shurtleff was explaining a new project to her fifth-grade art students. "We'll be making a design out of pasted pictures or scraps of paper or fabric," she said. "It's called a collage."

"First," Ms. Shurtleff instructed, "think of a theme for your collage. Second, gather your materials. You'll need scissors, glue, and poster board for the background. You'll also need magazines, colored paper or tissue, and scraps of cloth. You can also use small objects such as buttons and shells."

"Third," she continued, "cut out pictures and words from magazines to develop your theme. Next, add materials that will give your collage color, shape, and texture. Then move the pieces around on the poster board until you have the design you want. Last, glue the pieces to the poster board to create your collage."

The order of the steps to complete the collage is:

First, think of a theme for your collage.

Second, gather your materials.

Third, cut out pictures and words from magazines to develop your theme.

Next, add materials that will give your collage color, shape, and texture.

Then move the pieces around on the posterboard until you have the design you want.

Last, glue the pieces to the poster board to create your collage.

Read this story about a clever trick. As you read, think about what happens first, second, and so on. Then answer the questions.

The Mind Reader

Abe told his friend Corey that he could read minds and was ready to prove his power. First, Abe spread out nine magazines on the floor. He then arranged the magazines in three rows of three magazines each.

Abe's sister Sandra, who knew how to perform the trick, acted as his assistant. She placed a blindfold over Abe's eyes. Next, she turned him around so that his back faced Corey. Abe then asked his friend to touch one of the magazines.

After Corey made his choice, Abe turned around and removed his blindfold. He told Corey to concentrate on the correct magazine, but not to look directly at it.

With a measuring stick, Sandra pointed to the bottom right corner of the first magazine in the top row. "Is it this one?" she asked Abe. Abe answered, "No."

Sandra continued to point to magazines, from the top row to the bottom row. Each time, she asked, "Is this the one?" Each time, Abe shook his head "No." Finally, when the pointer touched the last magazine in the bottom row, Abe nodded his head and said, "Yes, that's the one."

Corey was astounded. He wondered how Abe had figured out that the correct magazine was at the bottom right.

1. What did Abe do first?
   - Ⓐ He put on a blindfold.
   - Ⓑ He placed nine magazines on the floor.
   - Ⓒ He asked Corey to touch a magazine.
   - Ⓓ He nodded his head.

2. In the story, which clue word tells what Abe did last?
   - Ⓐ first
   - Ⓑ then
   - Ⓒ next
   - Ⓓ finally

Work with a Partner

- Talk about your answers to the questions.
- Tell why you chose your answers.
- Then talk about what you have learned so far about understanding sequence.

REVIEW

Sequence tells the order in which things are done or events happen.

- Look for clue words such as *first, next, then, last, finally, before,* and *after.* These clue words help you figure out the order in which things are done or events happen in a reading passage.

- Look for clues that tell about times of day, days of the week, months, seasons, or years.

- When there are no clue words in a story, think about the beginning, the middle, and the ending to help you understand the sequence. When there are no clue words in an article, think about the order in which things happen or how things are done.

Read this article about how something was built. As you read, think about the clue words that tell you the order of events. Then answer the questions.

The Great Wall of China

About two thousand years ago, China's first emperor ordered the building of a huge wall along his empire's northern borders. After the wall was built, it was used to protect the Chinese from enemies in the north.

Over a million people worked on the project. The wall took years and years to build and eventually covered 3,900 miles. First, the builders piled dirt as high as 39 feet. Then they pounded the dirt into hard mounds. Each mound was about 32 feet thick. Next, the workers shaped the huge mounds with bamboo poles. Last, they fitted stones and clay bricks over the sides and the top. The top became a road that was wide enough for six soldiers on horseback to ride side by side.

Today, the Great Wall of China is still the longest structure ever built. People used to think you could see it from the moon!

3. What did the builders of the Great Wall of China do first?

   (A) They pounded dirt into hard mounds.

   (B) They created high piles of dirt.

   (C) They fitted stones and bricks over the sides and top of the mounds.

   (D) They shaped the mounds with bamboo poles.

4. Which clue word in the article tells what the workers did second?

   (A) then

   (B) next

   (C) after

   (D) last

Which Answer Is Correct and Why?

**Look at the answer choices for each question.
Read why each answer choice is correct or not correct.**

3. **What did the builders of the Great Wall of China do first?**

   Ⓐ **They pounded dirt into hard mounds.**

   This answer is not correct because the builders created high piles of dirt before they pounded the dirt into hard mounds.

   ● **They created high piles of dirt.**

   This answer is correct because paragraph 2 states, *"First, the builders piled dirt as high as 39 feet."*

   Ⓒ **They fitted stones and bricks over the sides and top of the mounds.**

   This answer is not correct because paragraph 2 states that the builders did this step last.

   Ⓓ **They shaped the mounds with bamboo poles.**

   This answer is not correct because the builders had to pile the dirt and pound it into mounds before they could shape the mounds with bamboo poles.

4. **Which clue word in the article tells what the workers did second?**

   ● **then**

   This answer is correct because this clue word tells what happened immediately after the workers created high piles of dirt, which was the first step. Pounding the dirt into hard mounds must be what the workers did second.

   Ⓑ **next**

   This answer is not correct because the word *next* is used in the article to describe what happened after the dirt was piled high and pounded into hard mounds. Shaping the mounds with bamboo poles must then be the third step.

   Ⓒ **after**

   This answer is not correct because the word *after* is used to describe what happened once the Great Wall was built.

   Ⓓ **last**

   This answer is not correct because the word *last* is used to describe the final step of construction of the Great Wall.

MORE TO KNOW	• If a reading passage does not contain clue words, ask yourself questions such as "What happened first?" and "What happened next?" to help figure out the order of events in a reading passage. • Stories are usually told in the order in which the events occurred—from the beginning to the ending. Not all stories are told entirely in time order; sometimes, a past event is introduced in the beginning or middle of a story.

Read this riddle and its solution. Then answer the questions.

One day, a farmer had to carry a goat, a wolf, and a cabbage across a river. The farmer, however, could bring only one item across the river at a time. He knew that if he left the goat, the wolf, and the cabbage alone, the goat would eat the cabbage, and the wolf would eat the goat. It took the farmer a long time to figure out a solution to his problem. At last, he realized how he could get himself and the goat, the wolf, and the cabbage safely across.

First, the farmer rowed across the river with the goat and left the animal alone on the opposite side. Second, he rowed back, picked up the wolf, and brought it across. However, he did not leave the wolf with the goat. The goat returned with him in the rowboat. Next, the farmer dropped off the goat and made another trip across the river with the cabbage only. He left the wolf with the cabbage and then went back to get the goat. After the farmer and the goat crossed the river again, they joined the wolf and cabbage.

5. Which of these did the farmer do first?
   Ⓐ He rowed across the river with the goat.
   Ⓑ He brought the wolf across.
   Ⓒ He left the goat alone.
   Ⓓ He brought the cabbage across.

6. What happened after the wolf was brought across the river?
   Ⓐ The wolf ate the goat.
   Ⓑ The farmer rowed back with the goat.
   Ⓒ The wolf joined the cabbage.
   Ⓓ The farmer went back to get the goat.

7. Which clue word in the story tells what the farmer did last?
   Ⓐ last
   Ⓑ next
   Ⓒ after
   Ⓓ finally

8. Before he tried to cross the river, the farmer
   Ⓐ bought a rowboat.
   Ⓑ separated the wolf and the goat.
   Ⓒ worried a lot.
   Ⓓ thought a long time.

Read this biography of a courageous woman. Then answer the questions.

A Fearless Conductor

Harriet Tubman helped free more than 300 slaves. She led so many slaves to freedom that she became known as the "Moses of Her People."

Harriet was born on a Maryland plantation around 1821. She was one of 11 children born to the slaves Harriet and Benjamin Ross. When Harriet was just six years old, she began working as a maid and a cook. At age 12, she went to work in the fields.

In 1844, the young Harriet married a freed black man named John Tubman. Five years later, Harriet Tubman heard rumors that she was about to be sold farther south, so she ran away. She traveled north on the Underground Railroad. The Underground Railroad was a network of safe hiding places leading all the way to Canada.

Tubman made it safely to Philadelphia. Once she was free, she grew determined to help other slaves escape. She became one of the leading conductors of the railroad. From 1850 to 1860, she made 19 trips back to the South.

Helping runaway slaves was against the law. Slave owners offered huge rewards for Tubman's capture. Tubman, though, was never caught, nor were any of her runaways. She later said, "I never ran my train off the track, and I never lost a passenger."

9. In the biography, clues that tell about the sequence are
   Ⓐ months.
   Ⓑ days of the week.
   Ⓒ times of day.
   Ⓓ years.

10. What happened in Harriet Tubman's life during the year 1844?
   Ⓐ She became a field worker.
   Ⓑ She got married.
   Ⓒ She fled to Philadelphia.
   Ⓓ She began leading slaves to freedom.

11. When did Harriet Tubman run away?
   Ⓐ 1821
   Ⓑ 1844
   Ⓒ 1849
   Ⓓ 1850

12. In 1860, Harriet Tubman
   Ⓐ became a railroad conductor.
   Ⓑ made her last trip back to the South.
   Ⓒ was captured.
   Ⓓ made it safely to Philadelphia.

TEST TIPS	• A test question about sequence may ask you when certain things happen in a reading passage. • A test question about sequence may ask you to put events from a reading passage in order. • A test question about sequence may contain words such as *first, second, last, before,* or *after*.

Read this tale adapted from a Chinese folktale. Then answer questions about the folktale. Choose the best answer for Numbers 13 and 14.

One day, three blind men stood together talking when one said, "I have heard about an animal called an elephant. I wish that I could touch it to learn what it is like."

"Yes," exclaimed the second blind man. "I would also like to touch an elephant."

"Me, too," the third blind man said enthusiastically.

A man who owned an elephant just happened to pass by and overheard the three men's conversation. "I have an elephant," the owner offered. "I will lead you to it."

The owner brought the first blind man to the elephant. The man reached out with his hands and ran them up and down the elephant's leg. "Now I understand," he said.

Then the second blind man took a turn. He was by the rear of the elephant, so when he reached out, his hands grasped the tail. "I know now," said the man.

When it was the third blind man's turn, his hands stroked the elephant's trunk. The trunk moved up and down, nearly lifting the man off the ground. "Oh," he said, "I get it."

The three men thanked the owner. As they walked away, the second blind man said, "I had heard that an elephant is strong, but it must be very weak. When I held the creature between my hands, it was not much bigger than a rope."

"You are mistaken, my friend," said the third blind man. "An elephant is very strong. It is as big and as long as a giant, powerful snake."

"You are both wrong," said the first blind man. "An elephant is like a thick tree trunk."

The men began to argue. And they may be arguing still. Each man was partly right, of course, but they were all wrong.

13. After the three blind men touched the elephant, they
    Ⓐ followed the owner.
    Ⓑ thanked the owner.
    Ⓒ argued with the owner.
    Ⓓ walked back to the owner.

14. The boxes tell about some of the things that happened in the folktale.

An elephant owner led the men to his elephant.		One man grasped the elephant's tail.
1	2	3

Which of these belongs in box 2?
    Ⓐ One man touched the elephant's leg.
    Ⓑ The three men stood together talking.
    Ⓒ One man stroked the elephant's trunk.
    Ⓓ The three men began to argue.

Read this article from a food magazine. Then answer questions about the article. Choose the best answer for Numbers 15 and 16.

Fast Foods for Fast Lives

Who first put ground beef between two slices of bread? No one knows for sure, but the hamburger sandwich first became popular more than 100 years ago. Factory workers especially liked this hand-held meal. They could buy two hamburgers for one nickel at traveling lunch carts. By the turn of the century, dining cars, called "diners," replaced the carts.

In 1916, J. Walter Anderson of Wichita, Kansas, invented the hamburger bun. Five years later, Anderson and a partner built a restaurant shaped like a castle and painted it white. White Castle® grew to become the first hamburger chain.

Soon after White Castle was born, the first drive-in restaurants appeared. These roadside stands used carhops to serve people in their cars. The drive-ins also had fun shapes and bright signs to draw in customers off the road.

In 1948, the McDonald brothers of California introduced a new kind of hamburger place. There were no waiters at their new restaurant. Customers ordered their meals at a walk-up window. McDonald's® could offer quick service because the food was sent to the restaurant ready to cook. The hamburgers were already shaped into patties. The french fries were cut and ready to be dipped in hot oil. Other restaurants sold their hamburgers for 35 cents. McDonald's hamburgers, though, were only 15 cents. French fries were a dime.

Dozens of businesses soon copied the idea of selling quick hamburgers at low prices. Today fast-food places are everywhere—highways, shopping malls, and even airports.

---

15. What appeared after drive-in restaurants?
- Ⓐ White Castle restaurants
- Ⓑ McDonald's restaurants
- Ⓒ dining cars
- Ⓓ traveling lunch carts

16. Before McDonald's opened,
- Ⓐ french fries didn't exist.
- Ⓑ restaurants weren't built on roadways.
- Ⓒ there were no hamburger chains.
- Ⓓ restaurant service took longer.

Read this article about Vietnam's early history. Then answer questions about the article. Choose the best answer for Numbers 1 through 6.

Two thousand years ago, the Chinese ruled the land that is now Vietnam. Many Vietnamese wanted freedom from Chinese rule. This dream burned strongly in the heart and mind of Trung Trac, the wife of a Vietnamese noble named Thi Sach.

In A.D. 29, a new Chinese governor took control in Vietnam. His name was Su Ting, and he was greedy and cruel. Trung Trac urged her husband to challenge the Chinese ruler. Thi Sach started to stir up trouble. Su Ting reacted by having Thi Sach put to death. The murder led Trung Trac and her younger sister, Trung Nhi, to raise an army of Vietnamese nobles and peasants. In A.D. 39, the Trung sisters led the troops in battle against the Chinese.

By A.D. 40, the Vietnamese had driven Su Ting out of the country. The Vietnamese kingdom was set up, and Trung Trac was declared queen. The new kingdom, though, did not last long. Within two years, the Chinese had sent the great general Ma Yuan into Vietnam with more than 20,000 soldiers.

Many Vietnamese felt they had no chance against such a large army. Because Trung Trac grew afraid that her followers would abandon her, she ordered an immediate attack. The Chinese easily defeated her small army. Several thousand Vietnamese soldiers were captured and put to death.

Trung Trac and her most loyal supporters retreated into the mountains. According to one story, Ma Yuan captured the Trung sisters and had them killed. Another story

says that the sisters died from disease. Still a third tale says that they disappeared into the clouds. The most popular belief is that the Trung sisters drowned themselves in a river rather than face the shame of surrender.

The Chinese controlled Vietnam for more than a thousand years altogether. Finally, in A.D. 939, General Ngo Quyen led the Vietnamese in a successful revolt against the Chinese.

Finding
Main Idea

Recalling
Facts and Details

Understanding
Sequence

Finding Main Idea

1. What is the article mostly about?
   - Ⓐ the rule of Su Ting
   - Ⓑ the Trung sisters' fight for Vietnam's freedom
   - Ⓒ the mystery of the Trung sisters' death
   - Ⓓ cruel Chinese rulers

Finding Main Idea

2. What is the best title for this article?
   - Ⓐ "The Trung Sisters"
   - Ⓑ "General Ma Yuan"
   - Ⓒ "The Death of Thi Sach"
   - Ⓓ "The Legend of Queen Trung Trac"

Recalling Facts and Details

3. Su Ting ruled Vietnam from
   - Ⓐ A.D. 39 to A.D. 40.
   - Ⓑ A.D. 929 to A.D. 939.
   - Ⓒ A.D. 29 to A.D. 39.
   - Ⓓ A.D. 29 to A.D. 40.

Recalling Facts and Details

4. Who led the Vietnamese in a successful revolt against the Chinese?
   - Ⓐ Trung Nhi
   - Ⓑ Thi Sach
   - Ⓒ Ngo Quyen
   - Ⓓ Ma Yuan

Understanding Sequence

5. Which of these happened last?
   - Ⓐ The Trung sisters raised an army.
   - Ⓑ The Vietnamese drove out Su Ting.
   - Ⓒ Su Ting took control of Vietnam.
   - Ⓓ Thi Sach stirred up trouble.

Understanding Sequence

6. After the Chinese defeated the Vietnamese army,
   - Ⓐ Su Ting regained control of Vietnam.
   - Ⓑ Trung Trac ordered an immediate attack.
   - Ⓒ Trung Trac retreated into the mountains.
   - Ⓓ Trung Trac was declared queen.

Read this German fairy tale adapted from the Brothers Grimm. Then answer questions about the fairy tale. Choose the best answer for Numbers 7 through 12.

Rumpelstiltskin

One day, a poor miller met the king. Wanting to impress the king, the miller said, "I have a daughter who can spin straw into gold." The king told the miller to bring the girl to his castle.

When the girl arrived, the king led her into a room full of straw. He gave her a spinning wheel and said, "If you value your life, you will spin all of this straw into gold by morning." Then he left her alone and locked the door.

The poor girl had no notion of how to spin gold out of straw. Her distress grew so great that she began to weep. Suddenly, the door opened, and in came a strange little man. "What will you give me if I spin this straw for you?" he asked.

"My necklace," said the girl. The little man took the necklace and then spun all the straw into gold. When the king came at sunrise and saw the glittering gold, he took the girl into a larger room filled with straw and asked her to do the same. Again, the little man came. This time, the girl gave him her ring in exchange for his help. The next morning, the king was delighted. He then took the girl to an even bigger room full of straw. "If you spin all this straw into gold," the king told her, "I will make you my wife."

The little man appeared for the third time. "I will spin this straw into gold," he said, "but you must give me your firstborn child when you are queen." The girl agreed, and soon she became queen.

A year later, the queen had a baby, and soon after, the little man appeared to claim the child. The queen began to weep so bitterly that the little man took pity on her. "Very well," he said, "I will give you three days. If you can guess my name within that time, you may keep your child."

The queen struggled to think of unusual names. She also sent a messenger to inquire about the little man. On the third day, the messenger returned with a story about a little man in the forest who had hopped around a fire on one foot and sung, "Today I brew, tomorrow I bake. And after that the child I'll take. I'm the winner of the game. Rumpelstiltskin is my name."

Not long afterward, the little man appeared before the queen. "Well, Your Majesty," he said, "what is my name?"

And the queen said, "By any chance, is your name Rumpelstiltskin?"

At that, the little man got so angry that he stomped off and never returned.

Finding Main Idea

7. The main idea of the fairy tale is found

- Ⓐ in the first paragraph.
- Ⓑ in the middle of the story.
- Ⓒ in the last paragraph.
- Ⓓ by thinking about the most important idea in the story.

Recalling Facts and Details

10. Which detail shows that the king was mean?

- Ⓐ He told the girl that if she valued her life, she must spin the straw into gold.
- Ⓑ He told the miller to bring his daughter to the castle.
- Ⓒ He was delighted to see all the gold.
- Ⓓ He took the girl's jewelry.

Finding Main Idea

8. What is another good title for the fairy tale?

- Ⓐ "A Greedy King"
- Ⓑ "A Little Man with a Strange Name"
- Ⓒ "The Talent of the Miller's Daughter"
- Ⓓ "Straw and Gold"

Understanding Sequence

11. What did the girl give the little man the second time he came to help her?

- Ⓐ her necklace
- Ⓑ her ring
- Ⓒ her gold
- Ⓓ her child

Recalling Facts and Details

9. Who first discovered the little man's name?

- Ⓐ the king
- Ⓑ the queen
- Ⓒ the messenger
- Ⓓ the miller

Understanding Sequence

12. The boxes tell about some things that happened in the story.

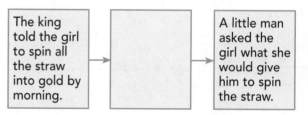

What belongs in the empty box?

- Ⓐ The girl gave the little man her necklace.
- Ⓑ A little man danced around a fire.
- Ⓒ The miller's daughter became queen.
- Ⓓ The king left the girl alone and locked the door.

RECOGNIZING CAUSE AND EFFECT

PART ONE: Think About the Strategy

What Is Cause and Effect?

There is a reason for everything that happens. What happens is called the *effect*. Why it happens is called the *cause*. You can find examples of cause and effect almost anywhere.

1 Write what a cat usually does when it sees a mouse.

_____

_____

_____

_____

2 Write why this happens.

_____

_____

_____

_____

Work with a Partner

- Take turns giving each other examples of cause and effect. You might say, "I saw a car skid because the road was icy."

- In each example, tell which part is the cause and which part is the effect.

How Do You Find Cause and Effect?

Many reading passages include examples of cause and effect. You can find causes and effects by thinking about what happens in a passage and why.

Read this passage about a bridge. Think about the things that happen and why they happen.

> The Winter Street Bridge is closed for repairs. Now lots of cars take a shortcut through the neighborhood streets. Many people complain about this traffic. They are worried that someone will get hurt.

1. Let's find an example of cause and effect in the passage.

   What happens? People complain about the traffic in the neighborhood. This is an *effect*.

   Why does it happen? People are worried that someone will get hurt in their neighborhood. This is the *cause*.

2. Let's find another example of cause and effect in the passage.

   Look at the chart below.

   The first box tells the cause for why something happens.

3. Fill in the effect in the second box. Tell what happens because the bridge is closed.

Cause	Effect
The Winter Street Bridge is closed for repairs.	Lots of cars _____ _____ _____

WHAT TO KNOW

What happens and why is called **cause and effect**.
Why something happens is the **cause**.
What happens because of the cause is the **effect**.

- A cause is the reason that something happens.
- An effect is the result, or what happens because of the cause.
- Clue words such as *so, so that, since, because,* and *if* often signal cause and effect. Other clue words are *reason* and *as a result*.

Read this article about a group of people who once lived in the Caribbean. As you read, think about one thing that happened to these people and why.

The Taíno once lived on the islands in the northern Caribbean. They were the first people to welcome Christopher Columbus when he arrived in the New World in 1492. The Taíno thought that Columbus and his crew were gods. They gave their visitors many gifts. The Spanish, though, treated the Taíno badly. First, they claimed all the Taíno land. Then they forced the islanders to dig for gold in barren mines. As a result, many Taíno died from being overworked. Others starved. Most Taíno died, however, because the Spanish brought diseases to the islands. By 1530, the Taíno population had almost completely disappeared.

One thing that happened to the Taíno and why is:

What happened: **By 1530, the Taíno population had almost completely disappeared.**

Why it happened: **The Spanish brought deadly diseases to the islands.**

Read these instructions for an art project. As you read, look for clue words to help you understand what happens and why it happens. Then answer the questions.

T-shirt Art

Here's a great craft idea for a party. Have your guests design their own T-shirts! You'll need plain white T-shirts, a set of fabric crayons, blank paper, pencils, and straight pins. Since you'll also be using a hot iron, be sure to ask an adult to help.

First, sketch a design on a sheet of paper. Be sure to draw any letters backward because the final design will be a mirror image of what you sketch. Second, color the design with the fabric crayons. Press down hard so that a thick coat of wax appears on the paper. Third, slide a sheet of paper inside the T-shirt so that the back of the shirt is protected. Then pin the finished design, crayon-side down, onto the front of the shirt. Secure the paper tightly so that the design won't shift or smudge. Next, turn on the iron. When the iron is hot, slide it back and forth over the sheet of paper. To check whether the design is transferring properly, carefully unpin one corner of the paper. If the colors aren't dark enough, for example, carefully replace the paper and iron some more. If your guests follow these steps correctly, everyone should go home with a wearable souvenir.

1. A sheet of paper is slid inside the T-shirt so that
   Ⓐ the design doesn't shift or smudge.
   Ⓑ the back of the shirt is protected.
   Ⓒ the fabric doesn't burn.
   Ⓓ the design is easier to pin onto the front of the shirt.

2. Which clue word or words in the instructions signal the reason that letters should be drawn backward?
   Ⓐ so that
   Ⓑ if
   Ⓒ since
   Ⓓ because

 Work with a Partner

- Talk about your answers to the questions.
- Tell why you chose your answers.
- Then talk about what you have learned so far about recognizing cause and effect.

REVIEW

A cause is the reason that something happens.
An effect is the result, or what happens because of the cause.

- To find a cause, look for a reason that something happened. Ask yourself, "*Why* did it happen?"

- To find an effect, look for a result, or something that happened. Ask yourself, "*What* happened?"

- Look for clue words that signal cause and effect, such as *so, so that, since, because, if, reason,* and *as a result.*

Read this report that Anya wrote about her mother. As you read, ask yourself, "*What* are some things that happened to Anya's mother? *Why* did these things happen?" Then answer the questions.

How My Mother Sees the World

At age three, my mother developed an infection that caused her to lose her sight. Since then, she has learned special ways to overcome her blindness.

Mom can enjoy books that have been recorded on CD or printed in braille. Braille is a reading system for the blind, based on touch. In braille, letters, numbers, and punctuation marks are printed as units of small, raised dots. Blind people read braille by running their fingertips over the dots. There is also a special computer for blind people that reads printed material aloud. But Mom doesn't own the machine because it's too expensive.

If my mom goes walking alone, she uses a special cane. It allows her to feel her way in unfamiliar places. Her friend Janice uses a guide dog. Recently, I read about a pair of glasses with a built-in device that sends out sonar waves. When the waves hit an object in the person's path, they bounce back in the form of sound. These sounds help guide the person wearing the glasses.

My mom doesn't think of herself as a person who cannot see. She says that she "sees" fine, just not with her eyes.

3. Anya's mother doesn't own the special computer because
   - Ⓐ it is too heavy to carry around.
   - Ⓑ she can read braille more quickly.
   - Ⓒ she prefers to listen to recorded books.
   - Ⓓ it is very expensive.

4. What happens when waves from sonar glasses hit an object in a person's path?
   - Ⓐ The waves spread out.
   - Ⓑ The object makes a noise.
   - Ⓒ The waves bounce back in the form of sound.
   - Ⓓ The glasses help the person to partially see.

Which Answer Is Correct and Why?

**Look at the answer choices for each question.
Read why each answer choice is correct or not correct.**

3. Anya's mother doesn't own the special computer because

    (A) **it is too heavy to carry around.**

    This answer is not correct because the report does not state that the computer is heavy to carry. The machine might indeed be heavy, but that cause is not revealed in the selection.

    (B) **she can read braille more quickly.**

    This answer is not correct because it is never stated in the report.

    (C) **she prefers to listen to recorded books.**

    This answer is not correct because it is not something that is mentioned in the report.

    ● **it is very expensive.**

    This answer is correct because it states the reason that Anya's mother doesn't own the machine. This cause is stated directly in the story, after the effect. The clue word *because* signals the cause-and-effect relationship.

4. What happens when waves from sonar glasses hit an object in a person's path?

    (A) **The waves spread out.**

    This answer is not correct because it is not a result that Anya mentions in her report.

    (B) **The object makes a noise.**

    This answer is not correct because the object itself never makes a sound. Instead, it is the waves bouncing back after hitting the object that are heard as sounds.

    ● **The waves bounce back in the form of sound.**

    This answer is correct because it tells the result of sonar waves hitting an object. This effect is stated in the report, after the cause.

    (D) **The glasses help the person to partially see.**

    This answer is not correct because the report never states or implies that the glasses help a blind person to partially see. Instead, the glasses help the person to hear sounds that bounce off objects in the person's path.

MORE TO KNOW	Sometimes, there are no clue words to signal cause and effect in a reading passage. When there are no clue words, do the following: • To find an effect, think about *what* happened. • To find a cause, think about *how* or *why* it happened. • Think about what you already know about how one thing might cause another thing to happen.

Read this article about why zebras have stripes. Then answer the questions.

In Black and White

Is the zebra a white animal with black stripes? Or is it a black animal with white stripes?

Scientists believe that an early ancestor of the zebra was a dark, horselike animal. This creature had no stripes. These solid-colored animals stood out in their surroundings. As a result, they were more likely to be attacked. Over time, some of these animals began to give birth to babies with light-colored stripes. Because the stripes helped to hide the young animals' bodies, it was harder for enemies to catch these animals. Since more of the striped animals survived over many generations, there were more and more striped animals. Eventually, the black-and-white creature known as the zebra was born.

5. The striped animals were harder to catch because
   Ⓐ their stripes helped to hide their bodies.
   Ⓑ their stripes made them stand out in their surroundings.
   Ⓒ their stripes blinded their enemies.
   Ⓓ their stripes were hard to see.

6. Which clue word or words in the article signal the reason that solid-colored animals were more likely to be attacked?
   Ⓐ since
   Ⓑ so
   Ⓒ as a result
   Ⓓ because

7. How did the zebra get its stripes?
   Ⓐ by living a long life
   Ⓑ by hiding in its surroundings
   Ⓒ by finding a way to confuse its enemies
   Ⓓ by gradual change over many years

8. Because scientists believe that its ancestor was a dark, horselike animal with no stripes, the zebra
   Ⓐ is probably a white animal with black stripes.
   Ⓑ is probably a black animal with white stripes.
   Ⓒ is probably a true horse.
   Ⓓ will probably become all black again over many generations.

Read this Greek myth. Then answer the questions.

Daedalus and Icarus

Daedalus was an inventor who designed a labyrinth for King Minos on the island of Crete. The king had ordered the maze built to hold the Minotaur, a monster who was half man and half bull.

At first, King Minos was pleased with Daedalus. His labyrinth had so many winding paths that the fierce Minotaur could never escape. Later, though, Daedalus offended the king. King Minos got so angry that he imprisoned Daedalus, along with his son, Icarus.

Daedalus immediately set to work on an escape plan. He made two pairs of wings by threading feathers together and fastening them with wax. Then he and his son put on their wings. Just before they flew off, Daedalus warned Icarus not to fly too high or too low. If he flew too low, the sea might wet his wings and make them heavy. If he flew too high, the sun's heat might melt the wax. The best thing, Daedalus told his son, was to follow him closely. Father and son then took to the air.

Daedalus flew ahead, but looked back constantly to keep an eye on his son. Icarus was so excited to be flying like a bird that he forgot his father's warnings. He climbed higher and higher in the air. At last, he came so near the sun that the wax holding his wings together melted. Icarus plunged into the sea and was drowned. Daedalus recovered his son's body and buried it on a nearby island. That island is now known as Icaria, and the sea into which Icarus fell is called the Icarian Sea.

9. The reason that Daedalus was sent to prison was that
   - Ⓐ he insulted the Minotaur.
   - Ⓑ he offended King Minos.
   - Ⓒ he allowed the Minotaur to escape from the labyrinth.
   - Ⓓ he played a foolish trick on King Minos.

10. Why did Icarus climb higher and higher into the air?
    - Ⓐ He was ignoring his father's request.
    - Ⓑ He did not realize that he was in danger.
    - Ⓒ He forgot about his father's warnings.
    - Ⓓ He thought that his father was mistaken about the danger.

11. What happened as a result of Icarus's flying too high?
    - Ⓐ His wings were burned by the sun's rays.
    - Ⓑ His wings became wet and heavy.
    - Ⓒ He became tired from the hot sun.
    - Ⓓ The sun melted the wax on his wings.

12. The island of Icaria got its name because
    - Ⓐ Icarus lived there.
    - Ⓑ Icarus fell there.
    - Ⓒ Icarus is buried there.
    - Ⓓ Icarus flew there.

TEST TIPS	• A test question about cause and effect may ask you *what* happened in a reading passage (the effect).
	• A test question about cause and effect may ask *why* something happened (the cause).
	• A test question about cause and effect often contains words such as *because, why, reason, what happened,* or *as a result.*

Read this article about a famous speech. Then answer questions about the article. Choose the best answer for Numbers 13 and 14.

The Gettysburg Address

The Civil War was a war between the northern states and the southern states. The people of the North and the South had different views. Mainly, they disagreed about slavery. In 1861, these differences caused the southern states to break away from the United States. The northern states didn't want the nation to be divided. As a result, the "War Between the States" began.

The greatest battle of the war took place in Gettysburg, Pennsylvania, in 1863. The North defeated the South in the Battle of Gettysburg. Both armies, though, suffered many losses. Over 60,000 soldiers died.

President Abraham Lincoln traveled to Gettysburg a few months later. He went there to dedicate part of the battlefield as a cemetery for the dead soldiers. It took Lincoln less than three minutes to give his speech. When he was done, there was hardly any applause. Lincoln thought that his speech had been a failure. He did not realize that most everyone was too deeply moved by his words to clap. Today, many people consider the Gettysburg Address to be the nation's greatest speech.

13. Why did Lincoln travel to Gettysburg?
    Ⓐ to congratulate the army of the North
    Ⓑ to dedicate part of the battlefield as a cemetery
    Ⓒ to help injured soldiers
    Ⓓ to cause the southern states to break away from the United States

14. Lincoln thought his speech had been a failure because
    Ⓐ few people clapped.
    Ⓑ it was too short.
    Ⓒ everyone seemed bored.
    Ⓓ the Civil War didn't end.

Read this story adapted from one of Rudyard Kipling's _Just So Stories_. Then answer questions about the story. Choose the best answer for Numbers 15 and 16.

In the beginning, when the world was new and the Animals were just beginning to work for Man, there was a Camel. He lived in the middle of a desert and he did not want to work. When anybody spoke to him, he said, "Humph!" Just "Humph!" and no more.

Presently, the Horse came to him, with a saddle on his back, and said, "Camel, O Camel, come out and trot like the rest of us."

"Humph!" said the Camel, and the Horse went away and told the Man.

Presently, the Dog came to him, with a stick in his mouth, and said, "Camel, O Camel, come and fetch and carry like the rest of us."

"Humph!" said the Camel, and the Dog went away and told the Man.

Presently, the Ox came to him, with the yoke on his neck, and said, "Camel, O Camel, come and plough like the rest of us."

"Humph!" said the Camel, and the Ox went away and told the Man.

At the end of the day, the Man called the Horse, the Dog, and the Ox together, and said, "I'm very sorry for you, but that Humph-thing can't work, or he would have by now. So you must work double-time to make up for it."

That made the Three very angry. Presently, along came the Genie in charge of All Deserts.

"Genie of All Deserts," said the Horse, "there's a thing in your desert with a long neck and legs who won't work. And all he says about it is 'Humph!'"

"Well!" said the Genie. "I'll humph him, if you will kindly wait a minute."

The Genie found the Camel looking at his reflection in a pool of water.

"My friend," said the Genie, "what's this I hear of your doing no work?"

"Humph!" said the Camel.

"You've given the Three extra work all on account of your idleness."

"Humph!" said the Camel.

"I shouldn't say that again if I were you," the Genie warned.

And no sooner had the Camel said, "Humph!" again than he saw his back puffing up into a great big humph.

"That's your very own humph that you've brought upon your very own self," said the Genie. "You will be able to work now for three days without eating, because you can live off your humph."

And from that day to this, the Camel always wears a hump.

15. Why did the camel get a hump?
   - Ⓐ It was his punishment for doing no work.
   - Ⓑ It suddenly appeared when he looked in a pool of water.
   - Ⓒ It was a gift from the Genie.
   - Ⓓ It was given to him by the three animals so that he could work longer.

16. What happened as a result of the Horse's complaining to the Genie?
   - Ⓐ The three animals got more work.
   - Ⓑ The Genie punished the Horse.
   - Ⓒ The Genie went off to scold the Camel.
   - Ⓓ The Camel became upset with the Horse.

What Is Comparing and Contrasting?

Thinking about the ways two or more things are alike is *comparing*.
Thinking about the ways two or more things are different is *contrasting*.
You can compare and contrast almost anything.

1 Write how a house cat and a lion are alike.

_____

_____

_____

_____

2 Write how a house cat and a lion are different.

_____

_____

_____

_____

Work with a Partner

- Take turns telling each other something that is the same about two kinds of animals. Then tell something that is different about the animals.
- See how many likenesses and differences you can find.

How Do You Find Likenesses and Differences?

Many reading passages compare and contrast two or more things. You can find examples of comparing and contrasting by thinking about the details you read.

Read this passage about Olivia and Rebecca. Think about how the two girls are alike and how they are different.

> Olivia and Rebecca are twins. They were both born on the same day, but Olivia is older than her sister by six minutes.
>
> Olivia and Rebecca look alike, but they are different in many ways. Olivia likes to play football and soccer. Rebecca would rather watch sports.

1. Let's think about the details that tell about the likenesses between Olivia and Rebecca.

   Now think about the details that tell about the differences between them.

2. Look at the Venn diagram below.

   The shaded part of the first circle tells how Olivia is different from Rebecca. The shaded part of the second circle tells how Rebecca is different from Olivia. These are examples of *contrasting*.

   The information where the circles overlap tells how Olivia and Rebecca are alike. This is *comparing*.

3. Fill in another example of comparing where the circles overlap to tell how Olivia and Rebecca are alike.

4. Fill in another example of contrasting in the shaded part of the second circle to tell how Rebecca is different from Olivia.

WHAT TO KNOW

Finding how things are alike and how they are different is called **comparing and contrasting**. Comparing is finding how people, places, objects, and events are alike. Contrasting is finding how they are different.

- Clue words that signal how things are alike are *both*, *same*, *like*, *alike*, and *similar*.
- Clue words that signal how things are different are *but*, *unlike*, *different*, *however*, and *whereas*.
- If there are no clue words in a reading passage to signal a comparison or a contrast, think about the people, places, objects, or events you read about. Ask yourself, "How are they alike? How are they different?"

Read this short article about the early buffalo hunters. As you read, think about the ways in which the Plains Indians and the hunters from the East were alike and the ways in which they were different.

At one time, more than 60 million buffalo lived on the Great Plains. For hundreds of years, the Plains Indians hunted the buffalo for food. They killed only the number of buffalo that they needed to survive. They also found ways to use the parts of the buffalo's body that they could not eat. The animal's hide provided clothing and shelter. Its bones and tissues were made into weapons and tools.

In the 1800s, hunters from the East came to the Great Plains. At first, they killed the buffalo mainly for sport. Later, they killed millions of the animals for their hides, which could be turned into leather. The hunters would cut off the valuable hide and then leave the rest of the body to rot. By 1895, fewer than 1,000 buffalo were left.

Ways in which the Plains Indians and the hunters from the East were alike:
They both hunted buffalo on the Great Plains.
They both used the hide of the buffalo they hunted.

Ways in which the Plains Indians and the hunters from the East were different:
The Plains Indians killed only the number of buffalo that they needed to survive, but the hunters killed many buffalo just for sport.

The Plains Indians used the buffalo's entire body for their needs, but the hunters used only the hide.

Read this article written by Ryan about his favorite sport—lacrosse. As you read, look for clue words that tell how lacrosse and baggataway are alike and how they are different. Then answer the questions.

My Favorite Sport

My favorite sport is lacrosse. I've been playing this sport as long as I can remember. Lacrosse is one of the oldest and fastest sports in North America. In Canada, it is the national sport.

Lacrosse is played by two teams on a large field. The object of the game is to throw a rubber ball into the opposing team's goal. Players use a long stick with a net basket, or pocket, on the end of it to pass the ball among teammates and move it down the field.

Lacrosse came from a rugged game that was played in Canada hundreds of years ago. The Algonquin, Huron, and Iroquois nations called the game "baggataway." The Native Americans used a playing stick similar to today's lacrosse stick. But instead of a rubber ball, they used a ball made of hair covered with deerskin.

Unlike lacrosse, baggataway was partly a religious ceremony. It was also an excellent way to get warriors into top physical condition. Baggataway teams were much larger than modern lacrosse teams. They sometimes had up to a thousand players! Several miles often separated the goals. Games could last for two or three days.

Some of the first French settlers in Canada played baggataway with the Native Americans. The French gave the sport its present name. They thought that the playing stick looked like a staff carried by French bishops, *la crosse*. As a result, the game took on a new name.

1. How are lacrosse and baggataway alike?
   - Ⓐ Both games last several days.
   - Ⓑ Both games are played by using long sticks and a ball.
   - Ⓒ Both games are played only in Canada.
   - Ⓓ Both games are played on the same size playing field.

2. Which clue word or words in the article signal that the purpose for playing lacrosse and baggataway is different?
   - Ⓐ but
   - Ⓑ similar
   - Ⓒ unlike
   - Ⓓ as a result

Work with a Partner

- Talk about your answers to the questions.
- Tell why you chose your answers.
- Then talk about what you have learned so far about recognizing cause and effect.

REVIEW

Comparing is finding ways in which things are alike.
Contrasting is finding ways in which things are different.

- Look for clue words that signal a likeness, or comparison, such as *both, same, like, alike,* and *similar.*

- Look for clue words that signal a difference, or contrast, such as *but, unlike, different, however,* and *whereas.*

- If there are no clue words in the reading passage, think about the ways in which the people, places, objects, and events are being compared and contrasted.

Read this poem about the ways in which an adult and a child question the world. In the poem, the questions are referred to as serving-men. As you read, ask yourself, "How are the views of the adult and child alike? How are their views different?" Then answer the questions.

I keep six honest serving-men
(They taught me all I knew);
Their names are What and Why and When
And How and Where and Who.
I send them over land and sea,
I send them east and west;
But after they have worked for me,
I give them all a rest.

I let them rest from nine till five,
For I am busy then,
As well as breakfast, lunch, and tea,
For they are hungry men.

But different folk have different views;
I know a person small—
She keeps ten million serving-men,
Who get no rest at all!
She sends 'em abroad on her own affairs,
From the second she opens her eyes—
One million Hows, two million Wheres,
And seven million Whys!

by Rudyard Kipling

3. In what way are the views of the adult and the child alike?
   Ⓐ Both ask the same number of questions.
   Ⓑ Both ask questions the entire day.
   Ⓒ Both take a break from asking questions during the day.
   Ⓓ Both ask questions, such as How, Where, and Why.

4. Which clue word in the poem signals that there is a difference between the views of the adult and the child?
   Ⓐ similar
   Ⓑ but
   Ⓒ unlike
   Ⓓ whereas

Which Answer Is Correct and Why?

**Look at the answer choices for each question.
Read why each answer choice is correct or not correct.**

3. In what way are the views of the adult and the child alike?

   Ⓐ **Both ask the same number of questions.**

   This answer is not correct because the poem suggests that the adult asks a few questions, but the child asks millions of questions.

   Ⓑ **Both ask questions the entire day.**

   This answer is not correct because the poem states that the adult lets his serving-men *"rest from nine till five,"* for he is busy then.

   Ⓒ **Both take a break from asking questions during the day.**

   This answer is not correct because the poem states that the adult gives his serving-men a rest after they have worked for him. The child, though, keeps her serving-men busy all day, *"from the second she opens her eyes."*

   ⬤ **Both ask questions, such as How, Where, and Why.**

   This answer is correct because the poem is about an adult and a child who both ask questions. The difference between them is the number of questions they ask.

4. Which clue word in the poem signals that there is a difference between the views of the adult and the child?

   Ⓐ **similar**

   This answer is not correct because the word *similar* is usually used to compare things, not contrast them. Also, the word *similar* is not used in the poem.

   ⬤ **but**

   This answer is correct because the word *but* introduces the line that signals a difference: *"But different folk have different views."* Note that the word *different* is also used to signal a contrast.

   Ⓒ **unlike**

   This answer is not correct because the word *unlike* is not used in the poem.

   Ⓓ **whereas**

   This answer is not correct because the word *whereas* is not used in the poem.

MORE TO KNOW	Sometimes, there are no clue words in a reading passage to signal that things are being compared or contrasted. When there are no clue words, • think about the people, places, objects, or events that you read about. Ask yourself, "How are they alike? How are they different?" • think about what is being compared or contrasted. Ask yourself, "In what ways are they compared? In what ways are they contrasted?"

Read this story about a contest winner. Then answer the questions.

Simon won a trip to an island in the North Atlantic Ocean. His choices were Greenland or Iceland. Simon didn't want to visit Iceland. Just its name made him feel cold. Greenland sounded like a much better place.

What Simon didn't know was that Greenland isn't really green. In fact, it's probably one of the least green places on Earth. Most of Greenland lies above the Arctic Circle and is covered with thick ice. In 982 A.D., the Viking leader Eric the Red established a colony there. He hoped to attract more settlers to the frozen island, so he called it "Greenland." The island population, however, stayed small. Today, most Greenlanders live near the southwest coast. It is the warmest part of the island. It is also the only area where grass and trees grow.

If Simon had studied his geography better, he would have known that Iceland is south of Greenland. Only the northern tip of Iceland touches the Arctic Circle. Iceland has far more green land than its neighbor. Part of Iceland is covered by ice, but the island also has hundreds of natural hot springs and volcanoes. Greenland is 840,000 square miles in area and has about 60,000 people, whereas Iceland is 20 times smaller in area and has at least four times as many people. Most Icelanders also live on the milder, southwest coast.

5. How are Greenland and Iceland alike?
   - Ⓐ Both lie mostly above the Arctic Circle.
   - Ⓑ Both are in the North Atlantic Ocean.
   - Ⓒ Both are the same size.
   - Ⓓ Both are mostly covered with ice.

6. In what way are the two islands different?
   - Ⓐ Greenland is smaller.
   - Ⓑ Greenland has more people.
   - Ⓒ Most people in Iceland live in the middle of the country.
   - Ⓓ Only Iceland has hot springs and volcanoes.

7. One thing the islands have in common is that
   - Ⓐ most people live on the southwest coast.
   - Ⓑ they were discovered by Eric the Red.
   - Ⓒ neither has any green land.
   - Ⓓ both have a large population.

8. In the story, the clue word *whereas* is used to contrast the islands'
   - Ⓐ size and population.
   - Ⓑ size and location.
   - Ⓒ population and climate.
   - Ⓓ appearance and location.

Read this chart which describes some of the ways that dolphins and porpoises are alike and ways that they are different. Then answer the questions.

Quality	Dolphins	Porpoises
Must surface to breathe	✓	✓
Have blowhole on top of head	✓	✓
Live in deep waters and near coast	✓	
Live mostly in coastal waters		✓
Swim at speeds up to 25 mph	✓	✓
Feed mostly on fish	✓	✓
Have a long, pointed snout	✓	
Have a short, rounded snout		✓
Have cone-shaped teeth	✓	
Have flat, spade-shaped teeth		✓
Have a long, thin body	✓	
Have a steeply sloping forehead	✓	
Have a gently sloping forehead		✓
Known for their intelligence	✓	✓
Can be trained to perform tricks	✓	✓
Produce sounds underwater and listen to the echoes to find food	✓	✓

dolphin

porpoise

9. Which of these tells one way dolphins and porpoises are alike?
   - Ⓐ Both have cone-shaped teeth.
   - Ⓑ Both live mostly in deep waters.
   - Ⓒ Both can perform tricks.
   - Ⓓ Both have the same size snout.

10. One way that dolphins and porpoises are different is that
   - Ⓐ only dolphins can produce sounds underwater.
   - Ⓑ porpoises have a more steeply sloping forehead.
   - Ⓒ porpoises swim faster than dolphins.
   - Ⓓ dolphins have a longer snout.

11. What three qualities do dolphins have in common with porpoises?
   - Ⓐ have blowhole, are intelligent, produce sounds underwater
   - Ⓑ must surface to breathe, swim at fast speeds, live in deep waters
   - Ⓒ have a rounded snout, feed mostly on fish, are intelligent
   - Ⓓ have flat teeth, have a pointed snout, live in coastal waters

12. Which of these is true?
   - Ⓐ Porpoises are different from dolphins in every way.
   - Ⓑ Porpoises do mostly the same things that dolphins do.
   - Ⓒ Dolphins look like porpoises.
   - Ⓓ Dolphins are just like porpoises, except that they are smarter.

TEST TIPS

- A test question about comparing and contrasting may ask you how things are alike or how they are different.
- A test question about comparing and contrasting usually contains a clue word. Words such as *same*, *like*, *alike*, and *similar* signal that you are to compare things. Words such as *different*, *unlike*, or *not like* signal that you are to contrast things.

Read this article about speed skaters. Then answer questions about the article. Choose the best answer for Numbers 13 and 14.

On the Cutting Edge

Until 1997, speed skaters wore skates in which the entire boot was firmly attached to the blade. Today, most speed skaters wear clap skates. The heel of a clap skate is not attached to the blade. A hinge with a spring holds the toe of the boot to the blade. When a skater pushes off, the heel lifts up, leaving the entire blade on the ice longer. When the skater's entire foot lifts off the ice, the blade snaps back to the heel, making a clapping sound.

a clap skate

On traditional speed skates, athletes push off from the back of the skate. They rely on their thigh muscles for power. On clap skates, athletes push from the front of the skate and use both their calf muscles and thigh muscles. The extra muscle power enables the skaters to extend their legs out farther. The more the leg extends, the longer the stride. The longer the stride is, the faster the speed.

Speed skaters who had trained on traditional skates had to learn new techniques to use clap skates. Some athletes had a hard time adjusting to the new skates. Unknown athletes who had figured out how to use clap skates began breaking world records.

13. In what way is a traditional speed skate different from a clap skate?
- Ⓐ A traditional skate is attached to the blade at the toe, but a clap skate is not.
- Ⓑ A clap skate is attached to the blade only at the toe.
- Ⓒ The boot of a clap skate is firmly attached to the blade.
- Ⓓ Only the traditional skate requires athletes to use their thigh muscles.

14. How are traditional skates and clap skates alike?
- Ⓐ Both have a blade that remains on the ice the same amount of time.
- Ⓑ Both require the skater to push from the back of the skate.
- Ⓒ Both pack the same amount of power and speed.
- Ⓓ Both have boots and blades as part of the skate.

Read this fable from Aesop, along with a Native American folktale. Then answer questions about both passages. Choose the best answer for Numbers 15 and 16.

One day, Hare made fun of Tortoise for being so slow on his feet. Much to Hare's surprise, Tortoise challenged him to a race. The Hare was amused at the idea. "Very well," he replied. "Let's try and see."

When the race began, Hare dashed off, leaving Tortoise behind. Soon Hare was so far ahead that he decided to take a nap. Meanwhile, Tortoise plodded on and on. When Hare awoke at last, he was surprised that Tortoise was nowhere in sight. Hare raced his fastest to the finish line, only to find that Tortoise had already won.

"Let's have a race," Hummingbird said to Heron one day.

"I won't race you," said Heron. "You are fast and nimble. I am slow and awkward."

Still, Hummingbird kept after Heron until he finally agreed to race for four days. The first one to reach the big tree by the bank of the river would own all the water.

On the first day of the race, Heron had barely taken flight before Hummingbird was off like a shot. Heron kept flapping his wings, and he soon found a slow and steady rhythm.

While Hummingbird was looking for food, Heron overtook her and went on past. Hummingbird took off again and was soon a considerable distance ahead of Heron, so she stopped to taste the flowers again.

While Hummingbird was looking for food once again, Heron kept on flying and soon went past Hummingbird. Hummingbird took off again and when she was ahead of Heron, she stopped to sleep for the night. But Heron traveled all night, passing the tree where Hummingbird slept. When Hummingbird woke the next day, she overtook Heron once again. This went on and on until the night of the third day when Heron kept on flying while Hummingbird slept once again.

On the morning of the fourth day, Hummingbird quickly reached the big tree along the bank of the river, but she was surprised to see that Heron had reached it first.

"We agreed that whoever got to the big tree first should own all the water," said Heron. "Since all of the water now belongs to me, you must not drink water but only taste the flowers when you travel about."

And that is why, to this day, Hummingbird drinks only the sweet nectar of flowers.

15. What is similar about the two stories?
   Ⓐ In both stories, a quicker animal challenged a slower animal to a race.
   Ⓑ In both stories, a quicker animal made fun of a slower animal.
   Ⓒ In both stories, Hare and Hummingbird rested each night.
   Ⓓ In both stories, the slower animal won the race.

16. The stories are different because
   Ⓐ the birds' race lasted longer.
   Ⓑ Hare wanted to race, but Hummingbird did not.
   Ⓒ Tortoise was slow, but Heron was fast.
   Ⓓ Hummingbird was less certain than Hare about winning the race.

MAKING PREDICTIONS

PART ONE: Think About the Strategy

What Is a Prediction?

A prediction is a good guess about something that will happen at a later time.
A prediction is often based on information you already know or have read about.

1 Write what you think will happen if you see dark clouds gathering in the sky.

_____

_____

2 Write the clues that make you guess this will happen.

_____

_____

_____

3 Is your guess always correct? Why or why not?

_____

_____

_____

 Work with a Partner

- Tell each other about something you thought would happen that actually did happen. You might tell about a homework assignment for which you knew you would receive a good grade. Or you might tell about a gift you received that was just what you expected.

- Take turns explaining why you thought these things would happen.

How Do You Make a Prediction?

You can make a prediction about a reading passage before you begin reading. Sometimes the title of the passage gives you a clue about what you will read.

Read the title, and then read this passage about a cat named Spike.
See if you can figure out what will probably happen next.

Finding Spike

Hannah looked everywhere for her cat, Spike. He had been missing for three days. She put up signs in the apartment building where she lived. She talked to all of her neighbors. One day the manager of the building called her. He said he heard strange meowing sounds in the basement.

---

1. Think about the title of the passage. The title tells you that someone or something is being searched for. You can figure out that you will read about a lost person, animal, or object.

2. Now let's think about what you read in the passage.

3. Look at the magnifying glass below. It shows the last sentence of the passage. See if you can make a prediction about what might happen next in the story.

He said he heard strange meowing sounds in the basement.

Predictions:

1. Hannah will search for her cat in the basement.

2. Hannah will find her cat in the basement.

4. Look at the box next to the magnifying glass.
   The box shows two predictions about what might happen next.
   The two predictions are almost alike. Both are good guesses,
   based on the story.

5. Reread the title and the information in the passage.
   How do you think the story will probably end?

6. Write your prediction on the lines below.

WHAT TO KNOW

When you think about what might happen next in a reading passage, you are **making a prediction**. Making a prediction is a way of using clues from a reading passage, as well as things you already know, to make a good guess about what might happen next.

- Clues are often in the title of a reading passage. Read the title, and then make a prediction about what you will be reading.

- Clues are often in the details of a reading passage. Details about the things characters do and say often help you make a prediction about what they might do or say later in the story.

- Clues are often in the pictures included with a passage. Pictures often show something that is happening or will happen soon.

Read this fable from Aesop. As you read, think about what might happen next.

Belling the Cat

Once upon a time, a group of mice got together. They met to discuss the best way to protect themselves against their common enemy, the cat. After several suggestions were made, a young mouse stood up and said, "I think I have an idea that will guarantee our safety. We should attach a small bell around the cat's neck. Its tinkling will warn us of her approach."

The other mice warmly applauded this proposal. They were about to approve it when a wise old mouse got up on his feet.

Think about what you just read and what you already know about cats and mice. Make a good guess about what might happen next. Then continue reading to see how close your guess is to what actually happens.

"I agree with everyone that the plan before us is very clever," said the wise old mouse. "May I ask, however, who is going to put the bell on the cat?"

What happened next in the story was that **the wise old mouse pointed out to the mice that someone would have to put the bell around the cat's neck.**

Read this newspaper article. As you read, ask yourself, "What does the headline tell me about what I will be reading? Which details will help me predict what will happen next?" Then answer the questions.

The Shipping News   **No More Dots and Dashes**   July 12, 1999

Today in North America, Morse code ends as the official language of the sea. For more than a century, ships in trouble have used Morse code. The code is used to signal other ships or rescue stations on shore. Now a new high-tech system will be replacing the famous code.

Morse code is named for its inventor, Samuel F. Morse. Morse developed the code in 1832 to send messages. Dots and dashes represent numbers and letters of the alphabet. The dots are short electric signals, and the dashes are long signals. With help from others, Morse later invented a telegraph machine on which to send his code. Morse code was not useful at sea, however, until the wireless telegraph was invented. This happened in the late 1890s. The most known Morse code message at sea is SOS, or dot-dot-dot dash-dash-dash dot-dot-dot.

International law will now require all freighters and passenger ships to have the new high-tech system. It automatically signals to rescue stations on shore when a ship is in danger. The signals give the ship's name and its exact location. With this new system, no ship should ever vanish without a trace. More lives will be saved.

The new system, though, still presents risks. Some poorer countries may not be able to afford the safer equipment. They may ignore the law. Crews and passengers could be in greater danger for a while.

1. What do you think has most likely happened since people stopped using Morse code?
   Ⓐ Sailors have had a lot of problems getting used to the new system.
   Ⓑ Morse code has been replaced on all ships.
   Ⓒ Ships have gone back to using Morse code because it's less risky.
   Ⓓ No ship has ever sunk again.

2. Where did you find clues to help you make your prediction?
   Ⓐ in the title of the news article
   Ⓑ in the picture that was included with the news article
   Ⓒ in the details about the high-tech signaling system
   Ⓓ in the details about what Samuel Morse did

Work with a Partner

- Talk about your answers to the questions.
- Tell why you chose your answers.
- Then talk about what you have learned so far about making predictions.

REVIEW

Making a prediction is a way of using clues from a reading passage, as well as things you already know, to make a good guess about what might happen next.

- Look for clues in a reading passage to help you predict what might happen next. Clues are often in the title, in the details, and in any pictures.

- Ask yourself, "What do I already know about the things I am reading about?"

Read this poem about a knight's search for a land of riches. As you read, look for clues that will help you predict what happened to the knight. Then answer the questions.

Gaily bedight,
A gallant knight,
    In sunshine and in shadow,
Had journeyed long,
Singing a song,
    In search of Eldorado.

But he grew old—
This knight so bold—
    And o'er his heart a shadow
Fell as he found
No spot of ground
    That looked like Eldorado.

And, as his strength
Failed him at length,
    He met a pilgrim shadow—
"Shadow," said he,
"Where can it be—
    This land of Eldorado?"

"Over the mountains
Of the moon,
    Down the Valley of the Shadow,
Ride, boldly ride,"
The shadow replied,—
    "If you seek for Eldorado!"

3. What probably happened to the knight?

Ⓐ He found Eldorado by going over the mountains and through the valley.

Ⓑ He realized that he had been dreaming.

Ⓒ He died a rich and happy man.

Ⓓ He died, having never found Eldorado.

4. How might things have been different if the knight had found Eldorado?

Ⓐ He might have never grown old.

Ⓑ He might have become very greedy.

Ⓒ He might have become happy and bold again.

Ⓓ He might have never needed advice from a stranger.

Which Answer Is Correct and Why?

Look at the answer choices for each question.
Read why each answer choice is correct or not correct.

3. **What probably happened to the knight?**

   Ⓐ **He found Eldorado by going over the mountains and through the valley.**

   This answer is not correct because the mountains mentioned in the poem were on the moon.

   Ⓑ **He realized that he had been dreaming.**

   This answer is not correct because there are no clues in the poem to suggest that the knight had been sleeping or dreaming.

   Ⓒ **He died a rich and happy man.**

   This answer is not correct because nothing in the poem suggests that the knight would find Eldorado. The shadow he met basically told him to end his search for Eldorado, for no such place existed.

   ● **He died, having never found Eldorado.**

   This answer is correct because details in the poem state that the knight had grown old and weak during his search. Also, the shadow tells the knight to ride *"Over the mountains/Of the moon,/Down the Valley of the Shadow."* These words suggest that Eldorado is not a real place.

4. **How might things have been different if the knight had found Eldorado?**

   Ⓐ **He might have never grown old.**

   This answer is not correct because no clues in the poem suggest that people stay young in Eldorado. Even if the knight had found Eldorado when he was still young, he would have still grown old.

   Ⓑ **He might have become very greedy.**

   This answer is not correct because the knight already was very greedy. He spent his life searching for Eldorado, a land of riches.

   ● **He might have become happy and bold again.**

   This answer is correct because details in the poem state that the knight was happy and bold when he began his search for Eldorado. After he grew old and had still not found the land of riches, he became heavy hearted. If the knight had found Eldorado, his spirits might have risen once again.

   Ⓓ **He might have never needed advice from a stranger.**

   This answer is not correct because there is no way to tell whether this prediction was likely. If the knight had found Eldorado, he would not have sought help from the shadow. However, he might have still needed advice from other people at certain times in his life.

MORE TO KNOW

- Look for clues in the reading passage that tell what the characters are like. Think about how the characters behave, how they are feeling, and what they say and do.
- Link the clues with what you know from your own experiences. Ask yourself, "What have people like this character done in a similar situation?"

Read this narrative about a true event. Then answer the questions.

The Mutiny on the *Bounty*

The year was 1789. The British ship *Bounty* sailed in the South Pacific Ocean. Its mission was to bring breadfruit trees from Tahiti to British settlements in the Caribbean. The captain of the *Bounty* was William Bligh. Captain Bligh was an excellent sailor, but he was a cruel commander. He controlled his crew with harsh treatment. Many of the men hated him.

One of the crew was Fletcher Christian. The other sailors respected Christian, and when he spoke that forbidden word—*mutiny*—the men listened. Mutiny meant taking over the ship. Mutiny was forbidden by law, but the crew had reached its breaking point. Mutiny it would be! If British sailors who mutinied were ever caught, they would be hanged. And a captain who could not prevent a mutiny did not escape punishment either.

The crew seized control of the *Bounty*. They put Captain Bligh into a small boat. Eighteen sailors refused to go along with the mutiny. So they were put into the boat with Bligh. The boat was set adrift in the vast ocean.

The mutineers had to hide where no British vessel would ever find them. Eventually, they sailed the *Bounty* toward a tiny mountainous island more than one thousand miles southeast of Tahiti. No people lived there. So it was that Fletcher Christian and eight other mutineers, along with six men and twelve women of Polynesia, came to live on Pitcairn Island.

Meanwhile, Captain Bligh and the others sailed their small vessel 3,500 miles to safety. Eventually, they returned to England.

5. What probably happened to the *Bounty*?
   - Ⓐ The mutineers sailed it to England.
   - Ⓑ The mutineers destroyed it.
   - Ⓒ The British navy found it.
   - Ⓓ The mutineers lived in it.

6. Which clue hinted that Captain Bligh would be able to sail his small boat to safety?
   - Ⓐ He would not escape punishment.
   - Ⓑ He was in a boat that was small.
   - Ⓒ Many of the men hated him.
   - Ⓓ He was an excellent sailor.

7. What most likely happened after Captain Bligh returned to England?
   - Ⓐ He was blamed for losing his ship.
   - Ⓑ He never sailed again.
   - Ⓒ He was given a new ship.
   - Ⓓ He was punished for being cruel.

8. If the British navy found the mutineers, the mutineers would probably have
   - Ⓐ surrendered without a fight.
   - Ⓑ apologized for what they had done.
   - Ⓒ seized control of the British ship.
   - Ⓓ been hanged for their crime.

Read this Greek myth about King Midas. Then answer the questions.

The Golden Touch

There once was a Greek king named Midas, who was famous for his beautiful rose garden. One day, the god Dionysus was traveling through the king's lands. His old teacher, Silenus, traveled with him. Silenus was a satyr, a creature that is half-human and half-goat. Like all satyrs, Silenus was often careless. In due time, he got lost and fell asleep in King Midas's rose garden. Some peasants found the satyr and took him to the king. King Midas recognized Silenus and treated him kindly for the next ten days. During this time, Silenus entertained the king with many wondrous tales. On the eleventh day, the king brought Silenus to Dionysus. Dionysus was grateful to King Midas for taking care of his teacher. So he offered to grant the king any wish. King Midas wished that everything he touched should be turned to gold.

Dionysus thought the wish was unwise, but he granted it anyway. Midas was so excited about his new power that he began testing it out at once. Everything he touched—the earth, his roses, the pillars of his palace—instantly turned to gold.

For a brief while, King Midas was happy. But then he began to regret his greedy wish. Whenever he tried to put any food or drink in his mouth, it also turned to gold. Despite all of his wealth, the king had to be fed like a baby. Then, one day, he truly realized how great a mistake he had made. He accidentally killed his daughter by turning her to gold when he touched her.

The heartbroken king pleaded with Dionysus to undo the wish. Dionysus took pity on King Midas and told him to bathe in the river Pactolus.

9. What most likely happened after King Midas stepped into the river?
   Ⓐ He drowned.
   Ⓑ His golden touch washed away.
   Ⓒ His greed disappeared.
   Ⓓ His daughter came back to life.

10. Which clue first hints that the king's wish would be a mistake?
   Ⓐ Dionysus thought the wish was unwise.
   Ⓑ King Midas began to regret his wish.
   Ⓒ The king accidentally killed his daughter.
   Ⓓ The king had to be fed like a baby.

11. If King Midas were ever granted a wish again, he would probably
   Ⓐ refuse to make the wish.
   Ⓑ make another greedy wish.
   Ⓒ make a wiser choice.
   Ⓓ wish that he had Dionysus's power.

12. If his daughter had not died, the king would have probably
   Ⓐ never asked Dionysus to undo the wish.
   Ⓑ still asked Dionysus to undo the wish.
   Ⓒ remained happy with his wealth.
   Ⓓ shared his wealth with others.

TEST TIPS	• A test question about making a prediction may ask you to make a good guess about what will happen next in a reading passage or what might happen in the future.
	• A test question about making a prediction usually contains the words *predict, probably,* or *most likely*.

Read this report about a famous woman in history. Then answer questions about the report. Choose the best answer for Numbers 13 and 14.

Reporting on a Remarkable Reporter

The woman whom I most admire was a reporter. She called herself Nellie Bly. I chose Bly for my report because I'd like to be a reporter, too.

Nellie Bly was born in Pennsylvania in 1867. Her real name was Elizabeth Cochran. When Elizabeth was eighteen, she read a troubling newspaper essay. It stated that women should not work outside the home. Elizabeth wrote back to the newspaper. In her letter, she stated her own views about women's independence.

The newspaper editor liked Elizabeth's writing so much that he hired her. He convinced her to take a pen name. She chose the name of a character from a popular song. "Nellie Bly" soon became known for writing about life in slums and factories.

As a reporter, Bly sometimes went undercover. In 1887, she pretended to be ill. By doing so, she was able to gain entry to a hospital for people with mental illness. Bly spent ten days as a patient there. Her articles about the experience led to many improvements at the hospital.

In 1888, Bly decided that she would circle the globe. She had recently read Jules Verne's adventure novel *Around the World in Eighty Days*. Bly hoped to beat the record set by Verne's imaginary character, Phileas Fogg.

Bly began her journey on November 14, 1889. It turned out to be a 24,899-mile trip. She traveled by boat, train, and even mule cart. On January 26, 1890, she returned home. She had set a record of 72 days, 6 hours, and 11 minutes.

13. Predict what Bly probably did next.
    Ⓐ She decided never to leave home again.
    Ⓑ She called Jules Verne to boast about her victory.
    Ⓒ She left her job as a reporter.
    Ⓓ She wrote news stories about her experiences.

14. Predict how most people probably reacted to Bly's achievement.
    Ⓐ They were angry that a woman had broken a man's record.
    Ⓑ They were excited to know a person could travel that fast around the world.
    Ⓒ They were convinced that she had cheated.
    Ⓓ They were upset that Bly did not realize that her place was at home.

Read this legend about a Swiss hero. Then answer questions about the legend. Choose the best answer for Numbers 15 and 16.

The Legend of Wilhelm Tell

Long ago in the heart of the Alps, there were three little countries called Schwytz, Ur, and Unterwalken. The people of these countries lived happily until Austria, their large, powerful neighbor, took control of their land. The Austrian governors ruled harshly. They forced their subjects to pay heavy taxes and obey unfair laws.

The most hated of the governors was a cruel man named Gessler. One day, Gessler stuck his hat on a pole in the marketplace. He told his soldiers to make everyone who passed by bow down before the hat.

One morning, a brave hunter from the mountains went to the marketplace with his son. The hunter's name was Wilhelm Tell, and he was famous for his skill with a bow. When Tell and his son passed the hat on the pole, they did not bow, for they did not know about Gessler's order. The guards stopped them and ordered them to bow to the hat, but Tell refused. So the soldiers arrested him and summoned Gessler. The governor knew of Tell's talent as an archer. He told Tell that he would set him free if he could shoot an apple off his son's head. If he missed, Tell would die.

While his son stood straight and still, Tell took aim. He pierced the apple right through the center. But Gessler could not accept his defeat. He spotted a second arrow hidden inside Tell's shirt and demanded to know why it was there. Tell boldly replied that if he had killed his son, the other arrow would have been for Gessler.

Gessler ordered his soldiers to arrest this villain. They bound Tell in ropes and put him aboard a small boat. As the boat was crossing the lake toward Gessler's castle on the other side, a violent storm arose. The soldiers could not handle the boat, and they begged Gessler to let them untie Tell so that he could help them row. Tell rowed hard and strong until he was close to shore. Then he dropped the oars, jumped onto the bank, and fled.

15. What do you think Gessler did next?
   Ⓐ He made his soldiers go after Tell.
   Ⓑ He told his men to leave Tell alone.
   Ⓒ He fell overboard and drowned.
   Ⓓ He shot at Tell with a bow and arrow.

16. If Tell was found, he would probably
   Ⓐ surrender quietly.
   Ⓑ beg for his life to be spared.
   Ⓒ defend himself.
   Ⓓ admit he was wrong.

Read this adaptation of a fairy tale. Then answer questions about the fairy tale. Choose the best answer for Numbers 1 through 6.

The Tiger, the Wise Man, and the Jackal

Once upon a time, there was a caged tiger. He struggled to escape through the cage's narrow bars, and he sobbed with rage when he failed.

By chance, a poor Wise Man came by.

"Oh, great one, let me out of this cage," cried the tiger.

"No, my friend," replied the Wise Man, "you would probably eat me if I did."

"On the contrary," swore the tiger. "I would be forever grateful and would be your servant for the rest of your days!"

The Wise Man still wouldn't let the tiger out. But as the tiger continued his wailing and sobbing, the Wise Man's heart softened. At last, he consented to open the cage door.

The tiger sprang out of the cage and seized the Wise Man. "What a fool you are!" cried the tiger. "Now there's nothing to stop me from eating you."

The Wise Man pleaded for his life. At last, he convinced the tiger to let the first animal that came by decide the fairness of the tiger's actions. The Wise Man promised to accept the animal's decision, no matter what.

Just then, a jackal came walking by. The Wise Man told the jackal his story. "How very confusing." the jackal replied. "Would you mind telling me over again?"

The Wise Man repeated his story, but the jackal still could not understand.

"Everything just seems to go in one ear and out the other," the jackal said. "Perhaps if I go to the place where it all happened, I shall be able to give you my opinion."

So they returned to the cage, where the hungry tiger was waiting. As the Wise Man began to explain the entire matter again, the jackal exclaimed, "Oh, dear! Oh, dear! Where are my wits? Let me see—you were in the cage, and the tiger came walking by—"

"No, you fool!" interrupted the tiger. "I was in the cage."

"Of course!" cried the jackal, pretending to tremble with fright. "I was in the cage. No, that's not right. Let me see—the tiger was in the Wise Man, and the cage came walking by. No, that's not it, either. Oh my! I shall never understand."

"Look here," the tiger shouted angrily. "I am the tiger. And that is the Wise Man. And that is the cage. And I was in the cage. Do you understand?"

"Well, no," the jackal replied. "Please tell me. How did you get in?"

The tiger finally lost his patience. He jumped into the cage and cried, "This way! Now do you understand what happened?"

"Perfectly!" the jackal declared, as he shut the cage door. Then he turned to the Wise Man with a smile and said, "Now let us leave matters as they were!"

Recognizing
Cause and Effect

Comparing
and Contrasting

Making
Predictions

Recognizing Cause and Effect

1. The Wise Man opened the cage door at last because
   - Ⓐ he wasn't very afraid of tigers.
   - Ⓑ he knew tigers didn't like to eat Wise Men.
   - Ⓒ he felt sorry for the sobbing tiger.
   - Ⓓ he thought the tiger would make a good servant.

Comparing and Contrasting

4. How were the Wise Man and the jackal different?
   - Ⓐ The jackal was more afraid of the tiger than the Wise Man was.
   - Ⓑ Only the Wise Man didn't trust the tiger.
   - Ⓒ Only the Wise Man was tricked.
   - Ⓓ The tiger thought that only the jackal was a fool.

Recognizing Cause and Effect

2. What happened when the Wise Man told the jackal his story?
   - Ⓐ The jackal appeared to be quite confused.
   - Ⓑ The jackal pretended to be afraid.
   - Ⓒ The jackal asked the tiger if the story was true.
   - Ⓓ The jackal told the Wise Man that the tiger had been unfair.

Making Predictions

5. Predict what the tiger would most likely do next in the story?
   - Ⓐ He will sob with rage.
   - Ⓑ He will trick the Wise Man again.
   - Ⓒ He will escape by bending the bars of the cage.
   - Ⓓ He will apologize for losing his patience.

Comparing and Contrasting

3. How were the tiger and the jackal alike?
   - Ⓐ Both lost their patience easily.
   - Ⓑ Both were clever creatures.
   - Ⓒ Both wanted to eat the Wise Man.
   - Ⓓ Both became easily confused.

Making Predictions

6. If the Wise Man came across a caged tiger again, he would most likely
   - Ⓐ free the animal.
   - Ⓑ ignore the animal.
   - Ⓒ seek the jackal's advice.
   - Ⓓ ask the tiger if it is hungry.

Read this article about two scientists. Then answer questions about the article. Choose the best answer for Numbers 7 through 12.

Women in the Field

Scientists Jane Goodall and Dian Fossey were both known for their work with apes. Goodall observed chimpanzees. Fossey studied mountain gorillas.

Jane Goodall was born in Great Britain in 1934. As a young girl, she dreamed of going to Africa to study animals. In her twenties, Goodall's dream came true. She took a trip to Kenya. While visiting the country, she worked for Louis and Mary Leakey. The famous couple was digging for human fossils. Louis Leakey encouraged Goodall to study chimpanzees in the wild. He got funds for her fieldwork, which began in 1960 in Tanzania.

Goodall worked for more than a year to win the trust of the chimpanzees she was studying. Finally, they allowed her to get close enough to observe them. Goodall made two surprising discoveries. She learned that chimpanzees eat other animals. Most scientists at that time thought that chimpanzees only ate fruits and vegetables. She also discovered that chimpanzees make and use tools. Goodall spent the next 25 years in the jungle, observing chimp behavior. She also raised awareness about the need to protect these wild animals.

Dian Fossey was born in San Francisco in 1932. As a young woman, Fossey read a book about mountain gorillas. It captured her interest. In 1963, she traveled to Africa to see the animals. She also visited Louis Leakey. In 1966, Leakey arranged for Fossey to study mountain gorillas. She would live with them in their natural habitat.

Fossey set up camp on a hillside in Rwanda. There, she quickly gained the trust of the gorillas by imitating them. Fossey was able to observe the animals at close range. She discovered that gorillas are not as fierce as they look. They are generally peaceful animals. After poachers illegally hunted and killed several gorillas, Fossey worked hard to protect them. She described her work in the 1983 book *Gorillas in the Mist*. In 1985, Fossey was murdered. Many people suspect that the poachers who had killed the gorillas killed her, too.

chimpanzee

mountain gorilla

Recognizing Cause and Effect

7. Jane Goodall went to Tanzania because
   - (A) she had always wanted to go to Africa.
   - (B) she wanted to work for the Leakeys.
   - (C) Louis Leakey had gotten funds for her to do fieldwork with chimpanzees.
   - (D) it was the only place where she could observe chimpanzees in the wild.

Comparing and Contrasting

10. What is one way that Goodall and Fossey were different?
    - (A) Only Fossey worked to protect the apes.
    - (B) It took Goodall more time to win the trust of her apes.
    - (C) Only Fossey observed the apes in their own environment.
    - (D) Only Goodall made interesting discoveries about the apes.

Recognizing Cause and Effect

8. How did Dian Fossey gain the trust of the mountain gorillas?
   - (A) by patiently waiting a year for them to accept her
   - (B) by imitating them in their natural habitat
   - (C) by working hard to protect them
   - (D) by observing them at close range

Making Predictions

11. Predict how Fossey felt when the gorillas were killed.
    - (A) She was deeply saddened.
    - (B) She was not at all concerned.
    - (C) She was slightly annoyed.
    - (D) She was overjoyed.

Comparing and Contrasting

9. How were Jane Goodall and Dian Fossey alike?
   - (A) Both worked in Tanzania.
   - (B) Both were British scientists.
   - (C) Both went to Africa in 1963.
   - (D) Both had Louis Leakey's support.

Making Predictions

12. Predict which of these most likely happened after Fossey's book was published.
    - (A) The poachers stopped killing the gorillas.
    - (B) People became more aware of the need to protect the gorillas.
    - (C) People refused to believe that gorillas are peaceful animals.
    - (D) More scientists went to Tanzania to study chimpanzees.

What Is Word Meaning in Context?

Sometimes when you speak with someone, you hear a word you've never heard before. Many times you can figure out the meaning of the word by how the person uses it.

1 Write what you think the word *majority* means. It's okay if you don't know the real meaning. Just make a good guess.

_____

2 Someone says to you, "<u>She won the election because a majority of voters chose her</u>." Write what you think the word *majority* means now.

_____

3 Write the clues in the underlined sentence that helped you figure out what the word *majority* means.

_____

_____

_____

Work with a Partner

- Make a list of five challenging words with meanings you know. Then ask your partner which words he or she doesn't know.
- Use each of the words your partner doesn't know in a sentence that gives a good hint about the word's meaning. Have your partner guess what the word means.
- Then have your partner do the same for you.

How Do You Find Word Meaning in Context?

You can find word meaning in context when you come to a new word in a reading passage. Look for clues to help you figure out what the word means. Clues might be in the sentence where the word is found. Clues might also be in the sentence just before or just after the one in which the word is found.

Read this passage about Tori. See if you can figure out what the word *mimic* means.

> My cousin Tori is five years old. She likes to do everything I do. If I make a face, she makes a face. If I cross my legs, she crosses her legs. When I do my math homework, she will try to mimic me by making scribbles on her paper. She even groans like I do when a math problem stumps me.

1. Let's narrow down the clues to figure out what the word *mimic* means.

    Look at the chart below.

    It shows three sentences: the one that comes before the word *mimic*, the one that contains the word *mimic*, and the one that comes after the word *mimic*.

    Look carefully at the sentences that come before and after the word *mimic*.

If I cross my legs, she crosses her legs.	When I do my math homework, she will try to mimic me by making scribbles on her paper.	She even groans like I do when a math problem stumps me.
Before		After

2. Now think about what the clues in the sentences tell you:

    Tori crosses her legs whenever her cousin does.
    Tori pretends that she is doing homework when her cousin does math homework.
    Tori also makes the same noises her cousin makes when a math problem stumps her.

3. So the word *mimic* must mean _____ .

WHAT TO KNOW

When you use clues in a reading passage to figure out the meaning of an unknown word, you are **finding word meaning in context**. The words and phrases around an unknown word often provide clues to the word's meaning. These clues are called **context clues**.

- Context clues are often in the sentence where the unknown word appears. They can also be in the sentences before and after the word.

- Clues about the meaning of an unknown word are often found by thinking about the way the word is used in the sentence.

- Clues about the meaning of an unknown word can be found by thinking about the details in the paragraph where the word is found.

Read this paragraph about Amelia Bloomer. As you read, think about the meaning of the word *advocate*.

Amelia Jenks was born in New York in 1818. In 1840, she married Dexter Bloomer. He was a newspaper editor who helped his wife become interested in social issues. Amelia Jenks Bloomer wrote many articles for the newspapers. She was a strong advocate for women's rights. She supported the idea that women should be able to vote. She even argued in favor of women wearing men's pants. Whenever she appeared in public, Bloomer wore loose pants under a short skirt. It wasn't long before these pants were known as *bloomers*.

You can figure out the meaning of the word *advocate* by looking at the words and phrases around it. The phrases *supported the idea* and *argued in favor of* are clues to the meaning of the word *advocate*.

The meaning of the word *advocate* is "a person who supports an idea or argues in favor of something."

Read this passage adapted from a Turkish folktale. As you read, ask yourself, "What clues will help me figure out the meaning of the word *submerged*?" Then answer the questions.

One night, Nasreddin Hoja was returning home after a long journey. He was tired and thirsty, so he stopped at the village well to rest and get a drink. As he used the rope to lower the bucket into the well, Hoja saw the reflection of the full moon in the dark water.

"Oh, no!" said Hoja. "The beautiful moon has fallen into the well. There is no time to waste. I must save the moon now!"

Hoja lowered the bucket deeper into the well until it was submerged just beneath the moon. Hoja raised the bucket, with the moon safely inside. But as he tried to raise the bucket further, it became lodged under one of the stones that lined the walls of the deep well. So, Hoja bent over the well and tugged on the rope. The bucket would not budge no matter how hard he pulled. Finally, Hoja placed one foot against the outside of the well and pulled with all of his might. The bucket let go as Hoja fell back onto the ground. He was lying there trying to catch his breath when he saw the moon glowing brightly in the night sky above him.

When Hoja got himself up, he brushed off his clothes and declared, "My work is now done. I have rescued the moon, and it is now back where it belongs."

1. In paragraph 3, the word *submerged* means
   Ⓐ "rescued something."
   Ⓑ "sank below the surface of a liquid."
   Ⓒ "pulled on a rope to lift something."
   Ⓓ "raised to the highest level."

2. Which word in the folktale gives a clue to the meaning of the word *submerged*?
   Ⓐ inside
   Ⓑ further
   Ⓒ deeper
   Ⓓ save

Work with a Partner

- Talk about your answers to the questions.
- Tell why you chose your answers.
- Then talk about what you have learned so far about finding word meaning in context.

REVIEW	The words and phrases around an unknown word often give clues about the word's meaning.

- Look for context clues in the sentence where the word appears. Look also in the sentences before and after the unknown word.

- Look for clues about the meaning of an unknown word by thinking about the way the word is used in the sentence.

- Look for clues about the meaning of an unknown word by thinking about the details in the paragraph where the word is found.

Read this poem about a forgetful boy. As you read, think about how you will figure out the meaning of any unknown words. Then answer the questions.

Godfrey Gordon Gustavus Gore
by William Brighty Rands

Godfrey Gordon Gustavus Gore—
No doubt you have heard the name before—
Was a boy who never would shut a door!

The wind might whistle, the wind might roar,
And teeth be aching and throats be sore,
But still he never would shut the door.

His father would beg, his mother implore,
"Godfrey Gordon Gustavus Gore,
We really *do* wish you would shut the door!"

Their hands they wrung, their hair they tore;
But Godfrey Gordon Gustavus Gore
Was deaf as the buoy out at the Nore.

When he walked forth the folks would roar,
"Godfrey Gordon Gustavus Gore,
Why don't you think to shut the door?"

3. In stanza 3, you can tell that the word *implore* means
   Ⓐ "argue."
   Ⓑ "excuse."
   Ⓒ "plead."
   Ⓓ "apologize."

4. Which word in the poem gives a clue to the meaning of the word *implore*?
   Ⓐ whistle
   Ⓑ wrung
   Ⓒ beg
   Ⓓ wish

Which Answer Is Correct and Why?

**Look at the answer choices for each question.
Read why each answer choice is correct or not correct.**

3. In stanza 3, you can tell that the word
   implore means

   Ⓐ "argue."

   This answer is not correct because
   the poem suggests that the mother
   is frustrated, but not angry enough
   to argue with her son.

   Ⓑ "excuse."

   This answer is not correct because
   the poem does not suggest that
   the mother is trying to excuse her
   son's behavior.

   ⬤ "plead."

   This answer is correct because the
   words and phrases before and after
   the word *implore* tell about begging,
   wringing of hands, and tearing out
   of hair. You can figure out from
   these details that the word *implore*
   probably means "plead."

   Ⓓ "apologize."

   This answer is not correct because
   the poem does not suggest that the
   mother feels any need to apologize
   for anything.

4. Which word in the poem gives a clue
   to the meaning of the word *implore*?

   Ⓐ whistle

   This answer is not correct because
   the word *implore* is used to indicate
   that the mother is saying something.
   It is not likely that she is whistling
   her words.

   Ⓑ wrung

   This answer is not correct because
   the word *wrung* is what the parents
   did with their hands. Since the word
   implore comes just before a statement
   the mother makes, *wrung* cannot be
   the correct clue.

   ⬤ beg

   This answer is correct because the
   word *beg* tells what the father did:
   the father begs, and the mother
   implores. It is logical to conclude
   that the two words have the same
   meaning.

   Ⓓ wish

   This answer is not correct because
   if you substitute the word *wish* for
   the word *implore*, the statement
   that follows makes no sense.

> **MORE TO KNOW**
>
> - Look for a synonym, or a word with a similar meaning, near an unknown word in a reading passage.
> - Look for an antonym, or a word with an opposite meaning, near an unknown word in a reading passage.
> - Once you think you know the meaning of an unknown word, read the sentence where the word appears and use the new meaning. Does the sentence still make sense? If so, you've probably figured out the meaning of the word.

Read this history of the railroad. Then answer the questions.

During the mid-1800s, people headed west in great numbers. Some traveled by covered wagon. Others sailed around the tip of South America. Both journeys were long and dangerous. Travelers wanted a faster and safer way to move west. In 1862, the United States passed a law to create a new railroad. It would stretch across the continent. The government offered land grants to two companies to build it. In 1863, the Central Pacific Railroad began laying tracks east from California. In 1864, the Union Pacific Railroad began laying tracks west from Nebraska.

At first, the two companies had trouble finding workers they could depend on. So the Union Pacific hired immigrants from Europe. The Central Pacific recruited Chinese laborers. Many of the men had already settled in California during the gold rush in 1849.

Part of the railroad had to go through the Sierra Nevada. The Chinese workers had the hazardous task of blasting tunnels through the hard rock. Men were lowered down cliffs in straw baskets. From there, they hammered holes into the rocky cliffs. They put dynamite into the holes. Then they lit the wicks of the dynamite. If the workers were lucky, they were pulled up to safe ground before the explosives went off.

In 1899, the Central Pacific track was finally linked to the Union Pacific track in Utah. The first transcontinental railroad was finally completed.

5. In paragraph 2, which clue word is a synonym of *recruited*?
- Ⓐ settled
- Ⓑ lowered
- Ⓒ hired
- Ⓓ offered

6. In paragraph 3, which clue word is an antonym of *hazardous*?
- Ⓐ blasting
- Ⓑ safe
- Ⓒ rocky
- Ⓓ hard

7. In paragraph 2, which word gives a clue to the meaning of *laborers*?
- Ⓐ companies
- Ⓑ workers
- Ⓒ trouble
- Ⓓ California

8. In the last paragraph, *transcontinental* probably means
- Ⓐ "crossing a continent."
- Ⓑ "crossing several continents."
- Ⓒ "where two sets of tracks meet."
- Ⓓ "from east to west."

Read this German fairy tale adapted from the Brothers Grimm. Then answer the questions.

The Elves and the Shoemaker

There once was a shoemaker who had grown so poor that he had only enough leather to make one pair of shoes. That evening before bedtime, he cut out the leather so that he could begin working on the shoes early the next day. When he awoke the next morning, he was surprised to find a beautiful pair of new shoes already made. Soon a rich customer came in and bought the shoes. He paid the shoemaker very handsomely. As a result, the shoemaker was able to buy enough leather to make two new pairs of shoes. Again, in the evening, he cut out the leather. In the morning, he found the job already done. For the money he received from selling those two pairs, the shoemaker was able to buy and cut out enough leather to make four new pairs. On the third morning, the shoes were again already finished on his table. And so the nocturnal visits from the mysterious helper continued. As many shoes as the shoemaker cut out at night, that many were ready the following morning. Soon, the shoemaker was prosperous again.

One night the shoemaker said to his wife, "Shouldn't we stay up just once to see who has been doing the work?"

So, the couple hid in the shop. Around midnight, they saw two elves appear, dressed in ragged clothes. The elves worked nimbly, and, in a flash, every shoe was made. Then, as quickly as they had arrived, the elves were gone.

The wife said to her husband, "These tiny men have made us rich. We must show our gratitude. The poor fellows must be cold in the rags they're wearing. Tomorrow, I will make them shirts, pants, coats, and stockings, and you make for each of them a tiny pair of shoes."

The following evening, the couple spread out the clothing. Then, eager to see how the elves would react, they hid themselves again and waited. Once more the elves came at midnight. When they saw the clothes, they quickly put them on. Then they began to hop and jump, and so they danced their way out of the door and never came back again.

9. In the first paragraph, you can tell that *handsomely* means
   - Ⓐ "beautifully."
   - Ⓑ "generously."
   - Ⓒ "gratefully."
   - Ⓓ "fairly."

10. In the first paragraph, which clue word acts as a synonym for *nocturnal*?
   - Ⓐ night
   - Ⓑ morning
   - Ⓒ mysterious
   - Ⓓ bedtime

11. In the first paragraph, which clue word is an antonym of *prosperous*?
   - Ⓐ new
   - Ⓑ surprised
   - Ⓒ rich
   - Ⓓ poor

12. In paragraph 3, the best meaning of the word *nimbly* is
   - Ⓐ "sleepily."
   - Ⓑ "slowly and clumsily."
   - Ⓒ "quickly and expertly."
   - Ⓓ "sneakily."

TEST TIPS

- A test question about finding meaning in context asks you about the meaning of a word as it is used in a reading passage. The word may or may not be familiar to you. The word might be used in a new way.

- A test question about finding meaning in context usually has several answer choices. Try each answer choice in the sentence in which the word appears. Decide which answer choice makes the most sense in the reading passage.

Read this poem about the building of skyscrapers. Then answer questions about the poem. Choose the best answer for Numbers 13 and 14.

Song of the Builders
by Jessie Wilmore Murton

O beams of steel are slim and black
And danger lurks on the skyward track,
But men are many, and men are bold,
And what is risk, when the stake is gold?
    So riveters ring,
    And hot bolts fly,
    And strong men toil,
    And sweat . . . and die . . .
But the city's towers grow straight and high!
O beams of steel are black and slim,
But the wills of men are stubborn and grim,
They reach forever to clutch the sun,
And what is life, if the goal be won?
    So riveters ring,
    And hot bolts fly,
    And strong men toil,
    And sweat . . . and die . . .
But the city's towers grow straight and high!

13. In line 4, what is the best meaning of *stake*?

Ⓐ "a pointed rod"

Ⓑ "a reward or prize"

Ⓒ "to claim as one's own"

Ⓓ "a thick slice of beef"

14. You can tell that the word *toil* in line 7 means

Ⓐ "to charge a fee for a service."

Ⓑ "to be lazy."

Ⓒ "to be afraid."

Ⓓ "to work hard."

Read this article about an important medicine. Then answer questions about the article. Choose the best answer for Numbers 15 and 16.

Victory over Smallpox

Smallpox was once one of the world's most dangerous diseases. It killed hundreds of millions of people throughout the world. Smallpox victims who got well again were often left blinded or badly scarred.

The first sign of smallpox was a high fever. A skin rash followed the fever. The rash then swelled up into watery spots. If the blisters began to bleed, the ill person soon died.

People who recovered from smallpox never got it again. Somehow, the first attack caused the body to defend itself against future attacks. For hundreds of years, doctors in Asia tried to protect healthy people against smallpox. Doctors would inject them with liquid taken from the blisters of smallpox victims. The procedure was risky, however. Usually the person got a mild case of the disease. But sometimes the person got a severe case of smallpox and died.

In 1796, a British physician named Edward Jenner improved on the Asian method. Jenner knew that men and women who milked cows often caught a disease called cowpox. Cowpox was similar to smallpox, but victims didn't get very ill from it. They just got a few skin blisters that soon went away. Some people believed that a person who had once had cowpox could not catch smallpox. Jenner tested this idea. He injected liquid from cowpox blisters into

the arm of a young boy. The boy became mildly ill but recovered quickly. Later, Jenner injected the boy with liquid from smallpox blisters. The boy did not become ill. Jenner repeated his experiment on other people many times with great success. He had created the first safe vaccine.

---

15. In paragraph 3, the word *inject* means
   Ⓐ "put a fluid into the body with a needle."
   Ⓑ "soak or drench."
   Ⓒ "force to do something against one's will."
   Ⓓ "add to a conversation."

16. In the last paragraph, the best meaning of *vaccine* is
   Ⓐ "a blister."
   Ⓑ "smallpox germs."
   Ⓒ "a medicine that protects a person from a disease."
   Ⓓ "a medicine used to clear up a rash."

DRAWING CONCLUSIONS AND MAKING INFERENCES

PART ONE: Think About the Strategy

What Are Conclusions and Inferences?

There are many times each day when you figure out something on your own without being told what is happening. If you see someone crying, you know the person is sad. If you hear someone laughing, you know that the person just heard something funny.

1 Write what you can figure out about the weather if you see people outside wearing shorts.

_____

_____

_____

_____

2 Write the clues that helped you figure this out.

_____

_____

_____

_____

Work with a Partner

- Take turns asking each other "What can you figure out?" questions.
- Ask questions such as, "What if someone is looking around the floor near the cage in which a hamster is usually found?"

How Do You Draw Conclusions and Make Inferences?

There are many times when you read that you draw conclusions and make inferences. Sometimes the author does not give you all the details. You need to figure out some things by yourself. An author might write about a snowy, cloudy day. The author does not need to tell you that the story takes place in winter. You can figure this out on your own.

Read this passage about Henry. See what you can figure out on your own.

> Henry sat on the front porch of his parent's house. He thought about the new job he would soon be starting. The sun began to set in the western sky. Henry could see the evening star in the distance. He wasn't sure if he wanted time to pass slowly or quickly. Tomorrow, Henry was moving away from his hometown, leaving his family and friends behind.

1. Let's draw a conclusion. Think about what the author tells you. Also think about what is just hinted at.

2. Look at the chart below.

   The first box lists details that are given in the passage.

   The second box tells what is hinted at but is not directly stated in the passage.

3. Think about what is given and what the author just hints at.

4. What you can figure out on your own? Fill in the missing information in the last box.

What details are given?	What information is not directly stated?	What can you figure out on your own?
Henry will be starting a new job. The sun is setting. The evening star can be seen. Henry is moving away and leaving his family and friends behind.	The author does not tell what time of day it is. The author does not tell why Henry is moving away and leaving his hometown.	The time of day is _____ Henry is moving away and leaving his hometown because _____ _____ _____

WHAT TO KNOW

Information is sometimes not clearly stated or explained in a reading passage. You must figure out some information on your own. Whenever you figure out something that is not told in a reading passage, you are **drawing a conclusion** or **making an inference**.

- Pay attention to the details in a reading passage. You can use these details to figure out information that is not clearly stated or explained.

- Use the details from the reading passage, as well as what you know from your own life, to draw a conclusion or to make an inference.

Read this fable from Aesop. As you read, try to figure out why the hunter was looking for the lion's tracks, but not for the lion itself.

The Hunter and the Woodcutter

A hunter was in the forest searching for signs of a lion. Before long, he caught sight of a woodcutter felling a tree. The hunter went up to the woodcutter and asked, "Excuse me, but have you noticed a lion's footprints anywhere about, or do you know where a lion's den might be?"

The woodcutter answered, "Come with me. I'll show you the lion itself."

The hunter turned pale, and his teeth chattered as he replied, "Oh, I'm not looking for the lion, thanks, only for its tracks."

Moral: *It is easy for the coward to be a hero at a distance.*

The fable does not explain why the hunter was looking only for signs of the lion and not for the lion itself. It does, however, provide details to help you figure out why this happened.

The hunter turned pale, and his teeth chattered.

It is easy for the coward to be a hero at a distance.

These details help you figure out that the hunter was afraid to actually come face to face with a lion and wanted only to hunt the lion's footprints. You probably also know from your own experiences that when people are scared, their skin may turn pale and their teeth may chatter.

Read this story about a young girl and her grandmother. As you read, look for details that will help you figure out how the girl feels about her grandmother's hobby. Then answer the questions.

Bess visits her grandmother almost every day after school. Bess spends a lot of time in the attic looking at her grandmother's treasures. One day, Bess came across a huge glass jar. In the jar was a collection of odd-looking buttons. "Why would anyone keep a jar of buttons?" wondered Bess.

Bess asked her grandmother about the button collection. She explained to Bess that they are reminders of her past and of how things have changed over the years. She then told Bess that no one really knows when buttons were first used.

"In some parts of the world," explained Grandma, "buttons have never been used. People have found other ways to fasten their clothing."

Bess wanted to learn more. She looked on the Internet and found that buttons became popular in Europe in the fourteenth century. From that time on, they have never gone out of fashion. Buttons are made from almost every kind of material. Some buttons are made of gold, silver, copper, brass, or other metals. Other buttons are made from cloth, bone, thread, or glass.

Bess looked at her grandmother's jar. There were so many colorful and unique buttons inside. Grandma smiled. She removed a large green and pink button from her collection and placed it in Bess's hand.

"This will help you get started with your own collection," she said. Bess looked at the button and smiled from ear to ear.

1. You can tell that
   Ⓐ Bess wants to write a report about buttons.
   Ⓑ Bess isn't really interested in having a button collection.
   Ⓒ Bess's grandmother will give Bess her button collection.
   Ⓓ Bess is excited to start her own button collection.

2. Which detail from the story helped you answer question 1?
   Ⓐ "Why would anyone keep a jar of buttons?"
   Ⓑ Bess looked at the button and smiled from ear to ear.
   Ⓒ "This will help you get started with your own collection."
   Ⓓ There were so many colorful and unique buttons inside.

 Work with a Partner

- Talk about your answers to the questions.
- Tell why you chose your answers.
- Then talk about what you have learned so far about drawing conclusions and making inferences.

REVIEW

Drawing a conclusion or making an inference is a way of figuring out information that is not stated in a reading passage.

- Think about the details that are stated in a reading passage. Use these details to help you figure out information that is not explained.

- Use the details from the reading passage and what you know from your own life to draw a conclusion or to make an inference.

Read this speech by Chief Joseph. As you read, ask yourself, "What details are stated? What information can I figure out on my own?" Then answer the questions.

> In the 1860s, gold was discovered on Nez Percé land in the Northwest. The U.S. government tried to force the Nez Percé to move to reservations. A band of Nez Percé, led by Chief Joseph, resisted. Eventually, fighting broke out between the Nez Percé and the U.S. Army. Chief Joseph fled with his people to safety in Canada, but they were pursued. Just 40 miles from the border, soldiers attacked the Nez Percé camp. Here is a speech Chief Joseph gave after that attack:

October 5, 1877

I am tired of fighting. Our chiefs are killed. Looking Glass is dead. Toohulhulsote is dead. The old men are all dead. It is the young men who say yes or no. He who led the young men is dead. It is cold and we have no blankets. The little children are freezing to death. My people, some of them, have run away to the hills and have no blankets, no food. No one knows where they are—perhaps freezing to death. I want to have time to look for my children and see how many of them I can find. Maybe I shall find them among the dead. Hear me, my chiefs, I am tired. My heart is sick and sad. From where the sun now stands I will fight no more forever.

3. From the speech, what can you tell about Chief Joseph?

   Ⓐ He was trying to convince the Nez Percé to keep fighting.

   Ⓑ He was not a strong leader.

   Ⓒ He wanted to surrender to the U.S. Army to prevent more deaths.

   Ⓓ He feared for his life.

4. You can conclude that Chief Joseph

   Ⓐ was angry that his people were suffering.

   Ⓑ blamed himself that so many of his people had died.

   Ⓒ was glad that his people had fought back.

   Ⓓ was deeply concerned about his people.

Which Answer Is Correct and Why?

**Look at the answer choices for each question.
Read why each answer choice is correct or not correct.**

3. **From the speech, what can you tell about Chief Joseph?**

   Ⓐ **He was trying to convince the Nez Percé to keep fighting.**

   This answer is not correct because the details give reasons why the Nez Percé should not keep fighting. Many of the Nez Percé were dead or were hiding. Those who remained were hungry and cold and had no strength to fight.

   Ⓑ **He was not a strong leader.**

   This answer is not correct because there is no reason to believe that Chief Joseph was not a strong leader. He never stopped caring about his people. He wanted to search for those who had run away to the hills.

   ⬤ **He wanted to surrender to the U.S. Army to prevent more deaths.**

   This answer is correct because details in the speech support Chief Joseph's statement that he is tired of fighting. He is saddened that so many of his people have died, and he just wants to end the killing by fighting no more.

   Ⓓ **He feared for his life.**

   This answer is not correct because there are no details in the speech to help you draw this conclusion. Chief Joseph seems to care more about saving his people's lives than his own life.

4. **You can conclude that Chief Joseph**

   Ⓐ **was angry that his people were suffering.**

   This answer is not correct because no details help you draw the conclusion that Chief Joseph was angry. He says, *"I am tired. My heart is sick and sad."* These statements show that he has no anger in him now. He just wants the killing to end.

   Ⓑ **blamed himself that so many of his people had died.**

   This answer is not correct because no details indicate that Chief Joseph thought that he was at fault for his people's deaths.

   Ⓒ **was glad that his people had fought back.**

   This answer is not correct because nothing in the speech suggests that this statement is true.

   ⬤ **was deeply concerned about his people.**

   This answer is correct because there is plenty of evidence to suggest that Chief Joseph was deeply concerned about his people. He was heartbroken about those who had died and worried about those who still lived.

MORE TO KNOW	• Look for details in a reading passage that tell about how a person or character looks, acts, thinks, feels, and speaks. Think about what you know about people with similar qualities.
	• Look for details in a reading passage that suggest where or when something happens. If something happens at Times Square, you can figure out that the setting is New York City. If something happens while the sun is shining, you can figure out that it is daytime.

Read this article about three famous men. Then answer the questions.

When Thomas Edison was a boy, he asked a lot of questions. His schoolmaster labeled him "too stupid to learn." As a result, Edison left school after only three months. Edison, though, was actually quite intelligent. He was an avid reader with a curious mind. Edison's curiosity led him to become a great inventor. With the help of his staff, he created over 1,000 inventions. He is most famous for inventing the electric light bulb.

Winston Churchill also did poorly in school. Although he was judged to have no promise, Churchill grew up to become a great man. Churchill served as prime minister of Great Britain during World War II. His leadership strengthened the spirits of his countrymen as the Germans bombed British cities. Churchill wrote a six-book history of the war. This effort won him the Nobel Prize in Literature in 1953. That same year, he was also knighted "sir."

Young Albert Einstein was a slow learner. He did not talk until he was four and did not read until he was nine. No one suspected that he would be one of the most famous scientists in the world. Dr. Einstein's theories changed the way people viewed the world. In 1921, this genius won the Nobel Prize in Physics.

5. Readers of the article can figure out that Edison
   Ⓐ took credit for his staff's inventions.
   Ⓑ wished he had stayed in school.
   Ⓒ asked questions because he was curious.
   Ⓓ was smarter than most of his teachers.

6. Details in the article suggest that Churchill
   Ⓐ became a gifted writer as well as leader.
   Ⓑ was supportive of the war.
   Ⓒ liked being called "sir."
   Ⓓ left school when he was very young.

7. There is enough information in the article to show that Einstein
   Ⓐ began forming physics theories during his childhood.
   Ⓑ did not appear to be a genius as a boy.
   Ⓒ never went to college.
   Ⓓ never wanted to be famous.

8. From the article, what can you conclude about all three men?
   Ⓐ They all won a Nobel Prize.
   Ⓑ They were all lazy as boys.
   Ⓒ They were all geniuses.
   Ⓓ They were all unsuccessful in school.

Read this humorous story from Great Britain. Then answer the questions.

Master of All Masters

A girl once went in search of a position as a maid. At last, an old gentleman hired her. On the girl's first day, the man firmly explained that in his house he had his own names for things.

He said to her, "What will you call me?"

"Master or mister, or whatever you please, sir," the girl answered.

"No, you must call me 'master of all masters,'" the man said. Pointing to his bed, he asked, "And what would you call this?"

"Bed or bunk, or whatever you please, sir."

"No, that's my 'barnacle.'" Pointing to his trousers, he said, "And what do you call these?"

"Pants or trousers, or whatever you please, sir."

"You must call them 'squibs and crackers.'" Pointing to his cat, he asked, "And what would you call her?"

"Cat or Kitty, or whatever you please, sir."

"You must call her 'white-faced simminy.'" Pointing at the fire, he demanded, "And what would you call this?"

"Fire or flame, or whatever you please, sir."

"You must call it 'hot chockalorum.'" He went on, pointing to the water. "And what is this?"

"Water or wet, or whatever you please, sir."

"No, 'pondalorum' is its name. And what do you call all this?" asked the man as he gestured toward his entire home.

"House or cottage, or whatever you please, sir."

"You must call it 'high topper mountain.'"

That night, the maid woke her master up in a fright. "Master of all masters," she shouted, "get out of your barnacle and put on your squibs and crackers. For white-faced simminy has got a spark of hot chockalorum on its tail, and unless you get some pondalorum, high topper mountain will be all on hot chockalorum!"

9. From the story, you can tell that the girl
    Ⓐ did not respect the man.
    Ⓑ was frightened by the man's behavior.
    Ⓒ was an obedient maid.
    Ⓓ had poor hearing.

10. Details in the story suggest that the man
    Ⓐ was quite peculiar.
    Ⓑ had never had a maid before.
    Ⓒ liked to play games.
    Ⓓ did not speak English very well.

11. What can you conclude about the cat?
    Ⓐ It was an orange cat.
    Ⓑ It had gotten too close to the fire.
    Ⓒ It was jealous of the girl.
    Ⓓ It liked to sleep on the man's bed.

12. There is enough information in the story to show that
    Ⓐ the girl had an excellent memory.
    Ⓑ the man should have fired his new maid.
    Ⓒ the girl will learn more unusual names.
    Ⓓ the man's house will be destroyed.

TEST
TIPS

- A test question about drawing conclusions and making inferences asks you to figure out something that is not stated in a reading passage.
- A test question about drawing conclusions and making inferences often contains the words *you can tell*, *determine*, or *conclude*.

Read this article from a math website. Then answer questions about the article. Choose the best answer for Numbers 13 and 14.

What Are the Odds?

When people want to know the chance that a particular event will occur, they often talk about "the odds." Two numbers are used to state the odds that something will happen. If the two numbers are close, the event is more likely to occur. If the two numbers are far apart, the event is less likely to happen. For example, the odds that a newborn baby will be a boy are 1 in 2. The odds that a pregnant woman will give birth to twins are 1 in 50. The odds of being hurt in a car accident are 1 in 75. These are all likely events. The odds of dying in a plane crash, though, are 1 in 10,000,000. Interestingly, the odds are greater for being struck by lightning (1 in 600,000) than for winning a major lottery (1 in 5,200,000).

Games played with number cubes are based on odds. Number cubes are small cubes with one to six dots printed on each side. The lowest number of dots that can appear faceup on a pair of rolled cubes is 2. The highest number of dots is 12. The odds that either number will be rolled are 1 in 36. The odds that a player will throw a 3 or an 11 are 1 in 18; and the odds that a player will throw a 4 or a 10 are 1 in 12. The odds that the cubes will total 5 or 9 are 1 in 9; and the odds that the total will be 6 or 8 are 5 in 36. The number that is most likely to be rolled is 7. The odds are 1 in 6.

Home   About Us   Search   Site Index   Help

What Are the Odds?

Fun Facts

Games

Activities

Quiz

Glossary

Links

13. There is enough information in the article to show that
   (A) a newborn baby is more likely to be a girl than a boy.
   (B) dying in a plane crash is an unlikely event.
   (C) a person is more likely to win a lottery than to be struck by lightning.
   (D) a person is more likely to be in a plane crash than to win a lottery.

14. You can conclude that when rolling number cubes, the odds are greater for
   (A) rolling a 2 than a 3.
   (B) rolling a 4 than a 5.
   (C) rolling a 7 than a 9.
   (D) rolling a 6 than an 8.

Read this story about a popular character in Arab folktales. Then answer questions about the story. Choose the best answer for Numbers 15 and 16.

Djuba's Guests

Djuba had a good friend who was a hunter. One day, the hunter visited Djuba in the city and brought him a nice fat hare as a present. Djuba roasted the hare and invited the hunter to stay and share it with him.

The next day, a man knocked at Djuba's door. Djuba opened the door and saw a stranger at his doorstep. "I'm sorry," Djuba told the man, "but I do not recognize you. May I ask who you are?"

The stranger smiled and replied, "Why, I am a friend of your good friend the hunter, who brought you the nice fat hare."

Now, the rules of hospitality required that Djuba invite this friend-of-a-friend in for a meal. But as the two men talked over dinner, Djuba realized that the stranger didn't really know the hunter very well at all. The man had only been after a free meal. Djuba was not happy, but he couldn't just throw a guest out of his house. He just smiled most hospitably and waited for the stranger to leave.

Djuba thought about his situation. "Now I have a reputation as an easy source for a free meal," he told himself. "I don't mind giving charity to the truly needy, but I do object to feeding every thief that appears at my door. How can I stop these crooks without being rude?" Djuba pondered this question, and, at last, he came up with a solution.

The next day, as expected, another stranger arrived at Djuba's door. "And who are you?" Djuba asked the man.

"Why, I am the friend of the friend of your good friend the hunter, who brought you the nice fat hare!"

"Welcome," Djuba told the man. "Come inside and join me for a meal."

Djuba placed a steaming bowl of hot water on the table. The stranger looked at the bowl with a puzzled frown. "What is this?" he asked.

Djuba smiled. "Why, this is the water that was boiled in the very same pot as the nice fat hare that my good friend the hunter, whose friend you know, brought me!"

15. From the story, you can tell that Djuba
   (A) does not like strangers.
   (B) does not trust most people.
   (C) is always generous.
   (D) is very clever.

16. Readers can figure out that
   (A) no more strangers appeared at Djuba's door.
   (B) Djuba and the hunter stopped being friends.
   (C) Djuba never invited another person into his home for a meal.
   (D) Djuba began offering meals to the truly needy.

What Is a Fact?

Have you ever told someone what grade you were in or how tall you were? If so, you were telling facts. A fact is something that can be proved. If you say, "I take the bus to school every day," you are telling a fact. It can be checked or proved.

1 Write one fact about a holiday you enjoy.

_____

What Is an Opinion?

Have you ever told someone how you feel about something? If so, you were telling an opinion. An opinion is what you think or believe. An opinion cannot be proved. If you say, "Baseball is more exciting than football," you are expressing an opinion. Everyone might not agree with you.

2 Write one opinion about a holiday you enjoy.

_____

3 Write how your fact is different from your opinion.

_____

_____

_____

Work with a Partner

- Take turns stating a fact about something, such as a pet or TV show.
- Then express an opinion about the same thing.
- Talk about how your facts are different from your opinions.

How Do You Find Facts and Opinions?

Some reading passages have details that are facts, and some have details that are opinions. Many passages contain both facts and opinions. Here's how to tell the difference: If a detail can be checked or proved, it's a fact. If a detail tells what someone thinks, feels, or believes, it's an opinion.

Read this passage about someone's bus route. See if you can tell the facts from the opinions.

> School starts every day at 8:05 A.M. I have to wake up very early to catch my bus. The bus comes at 7:00 A.M., and the route takes about one hour to complete. I think the town should add more buses so the routes can be shorter. It sure would be nice to sleep longer in the morning.

1. Let's think about which details in the passage are facts and which details are opinions.

   Look at the chart below.
   A check mark in the middle column indicates that a detail is a fact.
   A check mark in the last column indicates that a detail is an opinion.

2. Complete the chart by placing check marks in the appropriate boxes.

Detail	This detail can be checked or proved.	This detail tells what someone thinks, feels, or believes.
School starts every day at 8:05 A.M.	✓ Fact	☐ Opinion
I have to wake up very early to catch my bus.	☐ Fact	✓ Opinion
The bus comes at 7:00 A.M., and the route takes about one hour to complete.	☐ Fact	☐ Opinion
I think the town should add more buses so the routes can be shorter.	☐ Fact	☐ Opinion
It sure would be nice to sleep longer in the morning.	☐ Fact	☐ Opinion

WHAT TO KNOW

If a statement can be proved, it is a **fact**. If a statement tells what someone thinks or feels about something, it is an **opinion**. Facts can be proved. Opinions cannot. When you figure out if a statement is a fact or an opinion, you are **distinguishing between fact and opinion**.

- Facts are statements that can be checked or proved.
- Opinions are statements that cannot be proved. They tell what someone thinks or feels.
- Opinions often contain clue words, such as *think, feel, believe,* and *seem*. Other common clue words are *always, never, all, none, most, least, greatest, best,* and *worst*.

Read this poster for a school election. As you read, look for statements that can be proved. Also look for statements that tell what someone thinks or feels.

VOTE FOR PRESIDENT!

Hey, Class, it's time to elect a new president.

Voting day is only 3 days away!

Well, I think you can end your search now.

My name is Morgan Liberty, and

I'm your best choice for president.

I'm the most responsible person you'll ever meet.

I'll get the job done better than anyone else.

Believe me—vote for Morgan Liberty.

The statements that can be proved are:

Hey, Class, it's time to elect a new president.

Voting day is only 3 days away!

My name is Morgan Liberty.

The statements that tell what someone thinks or feels are:

Well, I think you can end your search now.

I'm your best choice for president.

I'm the most responsible person you'll ever meet.

I'll get the job done better than anyone else.

Believe me—vote for Morgan Liberty.

Read this friendly letter. As you read, ask yourself, "Which statements can be proved? Which statements cannot be proved?" Then answer the questions.

1489 Park Street
Any Town, VA 20000
October 10, 2009

Dear Sela,

Let me tell you about my teacher this year. Her name is Ms. Lightfoot. She's the most extraordinary teacher in the world. Ms. Lightfoot is so kind, funny, and patient that it's impossible not to like her. I also think she must be the smartest person to have ever taught in my school. She knows how to make every subject interesting, even geography! But she doesn't only teach us academic things. She also teaches us the importance of honesty, loyalty, kindness, and respect. She constantly reminds us to be true to ourselves and fair to others. She is the greatest human being.

All the kids in my class think Ms. Lightfoot is cool. She dresses in the latest fashions, and she never has a bad hair day. She's always up-to-date on pop culture. Every morning before the bell rings, she asks us trivia questions about recent TV shows, new movies, and hit songs. I'm getting pretty good at the game.

I hope you like your new teacher as much as I like Ms. Lightfoot. Write back and let me know.

Your friend,
Felicity

1. Which statement tells a *fact* about Ms. Lightfoot?

   Ⓐ She is the greatest human being.

   Ⓑ She is Felicity's teacher this year.

   Ⓒ She is the most extraordinary teacher in the world.

   Ⓓ It's impossible not to like her.

2. Which clue word in the letter signals an *opinion* about Ms. Lightfoot's intelligence?

   Ⓐ think

   Ⓑ seem

   Ⓒ best

   Ⓓ believe

Work with a Partner

- Talk about your answers to the questions.
- Tell why you chose your answers.
- Then talk about what you have learned so far about distinguishing between fact and opinion.

REVIEW	Facts can be proved. Opinions cannot be proved. • To find out if a statement is a fact, ask yourself, "Can this statement be checked or proved?" • To find out if a statement is an opinion, ask yourself, "Does this statement tell what someone thinks or feels?" • Look for clue words that signal an opinion, such as *think, feel, believe, seem, always, never, all, none, most, least, greatest, best,* and *worst.*

Read this article about an unusual bird. As you read, think about which statements are facts and which are opinions. Then answer the questions.

A Truly Swift Bird

The chimney swift has more energy than any other bird. Between the time it leaves its roost in the morning to the time it returns at night, this bird rarely lands. Instead, it tirelessly spends the day in flight. This sleek, gray-brown bird snatches insects in the air for food. It breaks twigs from trees for nests. It even takes a bath while flying. It glides down to water, smacks the surface with its chest, and bounces up, shaking the water off as it flies away.

Long ago, most chimney swifts nested in tall, hollow trees. After Europeans settled in North America, they cleared many of the trees to make room for farms and houses. But chimney swifts were able to adapt because they are the smartest species. They began nesting inside chimneys, which is how they earned their name. They attach their cup-shaped nests to a chimney's inner wall with their glue-like saliva.

Chimney swifts are the greatest acrobats. Unlike other birds, a chimney swift neither perches nor walks on the ground. They cling to vertical surfaces—like chimney walls—with the aid of hooked toes and stiff tail feathers.

Chimney swifts spend winter in South America. Every spring, they migrate 6,000 miles to North America. They often roost together in towns and cities. At dusk, you might spot a flock circling around a chimney's opening. The flock will abruptly spiral down into the chimney and disappear. The sight of a dark funnel of birds returning to their roost is amazing.

3. Which statement about the chimney swift can be proved?

   Ⓐ It has more energy than any other bird.

   Ⓑ It is the smartest species.

   Ⓒ It is the greatest acrobat.

   Ⓓ It migrates 6,000 miles in spring.

4. Which statement tells what the writer thinks or feels?

   Ⓐ The chimney swift spends its day in flight.

   Ⓑ Chimney swifts build nests in chimneys.

   Ⓒ The return of chimney swifts to their roost is an amazing sight.

   Ⓓ Chimney swifts do not walk.

Which Answer Is Correct and Why?

Look at the answer choices for each question.
Read why each answer choice is correct or not correct.

3. **Which statement about the chimney swift can be proved?**

   Ⓐ **It has more energy than any other bird.**

   This answer is not correct because it cannot be proved. The chimney swift may have a lot of energy, but another bird may be just as active, if not more. In fact, no one can truly prove which bird has the most energy.

   Ⓑ **It is the smartest species.**

   This answer is not correct because it cannot be proved. Chimney swifts did adapt to changes in their habitat when their nesting trees were cleared; however, it is impossible to conclude from this that the chimney swift is the smartest species over any other bird, reptile, mammal, or other animal.

   Ⓒ **It is the greatest acrobat.**

   This answer is not correct because it cannot be proved. It's true that the chimney swift clings to vertical surfaces and is acrobatic, but some other creature may be just as agile, if not more. Plus, who's to say which bird or animal is the greatest acrobat?

   ⬤ **It migrates 6,000 miles in spring.**

   This answer is correct because you can prove that the statement is true. The migration route can be measured or observed, and you can find facts about the bird in a book, in an encyclopedia, or on the Internet.

4. **Which statement tells what the writer thinks or feels?**

   Ⓐ **The chimney swift spends its day in flight.**

   This answer is not correct because the statement is a fact, not an opinion. Proof is provided in the description of how chimney swifts feed, gather nesting materials, and bathe while flying. You can also check this fact in a book, in an encyclopedia, or on the Internet.

   Ⓑ **Chimney swifts build nests in chimneys.**

   This answer is not correct because it can be proved. You can observe the bird's nest, or you can find facts about chimney swifts and their nests in a book, in an encyclopedia, or on the Internet.

   ⬤ **The return of chimney swifts to their roost is an amazing sight.**

   This answer is correct because the statement cannot be proved. The statement is the writer's opinion about watching a flock of chimney swifts return to their roost at night. A scientist who studies animal behavior may not think this sight is amazing at all.

   Ⓓ **Chimney swifts do not walk.**

   This answer is not correct because the statement can be proved. The article states that chimney swifts neither perch nor walk on the ground. This fact can also be observed and checked in a book, in an encyclopedia, or on the Internet.

MORE TO KNOW	• Facts can be observed, checked, or tested. You can prove that a fact is correct or true.
	• Opinions express someone's thoughts, feelings, or beliefs. An opinion can be about an event, an idea, a person, or a thing. Even though people might agree or disagree with an opinion, it still cannot be proved.

Read this report written by Roberto. Then answer the questions.

A Tribute to a Hero

Roberto Clemente was the finest athlete to grace the sport of baseball. I'm proud to be named in his memory. He is a hero to all Latinos, like me.

Clemente was born in Puerto Rico in 1934. He began playing for the Pittsburgh Pirates in 1955. Clemente had a back injury from a 1954 car accident, so he often played in great pain. Still, he always gave his best effort. Clemente had a strong throwing arm and was an excellent batter. He helped the Pirates win the World Series twice, in 1960 and in 1971. In 1966, Clemente won the Most Valuable Player award. In 1972, he made his 3,000th hit. Only ten other men had achieved that many hits.

Clemente was not just a great baseball player; he was also the world's most generous man. Every winter, he returned to Puerto Rico to teach baseball to the island's youth. He also planned the building of a sports center for them. When an earthquake struck Nicaragua in 1972, Clemente collected supplies for the victims. Then he rented a cargo plane to deliver the supplies. Shortly after taking off, the plane crashed into the ocean, and Clemente drowned.

All sports fans mourned his death. Within three months, Clemente was elected into the National Baseball Hall of Fame. He was the first Latino to earn this honor.

5. Which of these statements about Clemente cannot be proved?
   Ⓐ He made 3,000 hits.
   Ⓑ He played for the Pirates.
   Ⓒ He is a hero to all Latinos.
   Ⓓ He won a Most Valuable Player award.

6. Which tells an *opinion* from the report?
   Ⓐ He was the finest athlete to grace the sport of baseball.
   Ⓑ He had a strong throwing arm.
   Ⓒ He returned to Puerto Rico every winter.
   Ⓓ He helped the Pirates win the World Series twice.

7. Which of these clue words from the article signals an *opinion* about Clemente's generosity?
   Ⓐ more
   Ⓑ most
   Ⓒ always
   Ⓓ never

8. Which statement tells a *fact* about Clemente?
   Ⓐ He always gave his best effort.
   Ⓑ He was the world's most generous man.
   Ⓒ He was born in Puerto Rico in 1934.
   Ⓓ All sports fans mourned his death.

Read this courtroom conversation. Then answer the questions.

DOG: Your Honor, I'm here to complain about Porcupine's behavior. I believe that he's a danger to society.

PORCUPINE: A danger? Why, I've never done anything wrong in my life!

DOG: Is that a fact? Then how do you explain these quills I'm wearing?

JUDGE: Yes, Porcupine, how did those quills get stuck in Dog's skin?

PORCUPINE: Your Honor, it seems to me that Dog was at fault for his injury. He's wearing my quills because he got too close to me.

DOG: You tell the biggest fibs! You know that you shot your quills at me.

PORCUPINE: You're always making ridiculous statements. Everyone knows that porcupines can't shoot their quills.

JUDGE: He's right, Dog. I think you owe Porcupine an apology.

DOG: But, Judge, Porcupine still caused me harm. When he spotted me in the woods last night, his quills stood straight up, like pins in a pincushion. Then he turned his back to me and shook his tail. The next thing I knew, his sharp quills were piercing my skin. Believe me, the pain is worse than anything anyone has ever felt.

PORCUPINE: Oh, stop whining, Dog. You're always complaining.

JUDGE: Porcupine, did you use your quills as weapons?

PORCUPINE: Not exactly, Your Honor. Dog didn't tell you why I bumped into him. I was afraid because he had threatened me. And when I'm frightened, my quills stand straight up and come loose easily.

JUDGE: So, Dog, what do you have to say for yourself?

And for once, Dog had nothing to say.

9. Which statement about Porcupine can be proved?
   - Ⓐ He's a danger to society.
   - Ⓑ His quills stand up straight when he's frightened.
   - Ⓒ He's never done anything wrong in his life.
   - Ⓓ He tells the biggest fibs.

10. Which statement cannot be proved?
   - Ⓐ Porcupine's quills come loose easily when he is frightened.
   - Ⓑ Dog didn't tell all the facts at first.
   - Ⓒ Porcupine and Dog met in the woods.
   - Ⓓ Dog's pain is worse than anything anyone has ever felt.

11. Which of these is an *opinion* from the passage?
   - Ⓐ Porcupine bumped into Dog because he was afraid.
   - Ⓑ Dog admitted that he might have growled at Porcupine.
   - Ⓒ Everyone knows that porcupines can't shoot their quills.
   - Ⓓ Dog didn't touch Porcupine.

12. Which statement tells a *fact* about Dog?
   - Ⓐ He was hurt by Porcupine's quills.
   - Ⓑ He has nothing to say.
   - Ⓒ He is always complaining.
   - Ⓓ He is always making ridiculous statements.

- A test question about distinguishing between fact and opinion may ask you to identify which of four statements is a fact or an opinion.

- To recognize a *fact*, read each answer choice and ask yourself, "Can this statement be proved?" If it can, then it is a fact.

- To recognize an *opinion*, read each answer choice and ask yourself, "Does this statement tell what someone thinks or feels?" If it does, then it is an opinion. Also, look for clue words in the answer choices that signal an opinion.

Read this journal entry by Peter. Then answer questions about the journal entry. Choose the best answer for Numbers 13 and 14.

January 14, 2010

I'm tired of being treated like a child in my family. Even though my brother is only two years older than I am, my parents act as if I'm a lot younger. It seems to me that my brother always gets to do whatever he wants to do. Stephen stays up late at night. I have to go to bed by 9:00 P.M. Stephen goes to all the latest movies. Every time I want to go with him, my parents say that I'm not old enough. My brother can also ride his bike anywhere in town. I'm only allowed to ride to and from school. I never get to go anywhere alone. Stephen goes many places by himself.

Besides having all kinds of freedom while I have none, Stephen also gets a bigger allowance. I think that by giving me less spending money, my parents are making certain that I can't afford to do anything. Every time I complain to my parents that they treat Stephen and me differently, they say the same thing. "When you're older, you'll get to have these privileges, too."

The worst insult is that Stephen bosses me around all the time. "Do this, Peter. Do that, Peter." I'm sick of it. The Constitution says that all men are created equal. So why doesn't this apply to younger brothers?

13. Which of these is an *opinion* from the journal entry?
   Ⓐ Stephen is only two years older than Peter.
   Ⓑ Stephen always gets to do whatever he wants to do.
   Ⓒ Stephen stays up late at night.
   Ⓓ Stephen goes many places by himself.

14. Which of these is a *fact* from the journal entry?
   Ⓐ Peter has no freedom.
   Ⓑ Every time Peter wants to see a film, he's told he's not old enough.
   Ⓒ Stephen gets a bigger allowance than Peter.
   Ⓓ Stephen bosses Peter around all the time.

Read this book report. Then answer questions about the book report. Choose the best answer for Numbers 15 and 16.

I just read the most exciting book ever written. It has everything I like in a book—humor, adventure, romance, and magic. The book is a huge collection of ancient folktales from Arabia, India, and Persia. It's called *The Thousand and One Nights.*

The book begins with the story of a king who was betrayed by his queen. The king was so bitter that he vowed to marry a new maiden each night. The next morning, he would have her beheaded. One bride, named Scheherazade, however, was more clever than all the others. She delayed having her head chopped off by telling her new husband a story. The king was so delighted by his bride's tale that he allowed her to live another day to finish it. Scheherazade wove one tale after another for a thousand and one nights. In this way, she saved her life and won the king's love.

Three of the most popular tales from *The Thousand and One Nights* are "Aladdin," "Sinbad the Sailor," and "Ali Baba and the Forty Thieves." I thought "Aladdin" was the best story. It is about a poor but idle boy named Aladdin. One day, he meets a cunning magician, who claims to be his uncle. The magician tricks Aladdin into entering an underground cave to recover an old lamp. When Aladdin returns to the mouth of the cave with the lamp, the magician demands that he hand it over immediately. But Aladdin refuses to give up the lamp until he is out of the cave safely. The magician flies into a rage and traps Aladdin in the dark cave. By accident, Aladdin discovers that when the lamp is rubbed, an enormous genie appears. The genie promises to obey Aladdin in all ways. With the genie's help, Aladdin eventually gains wealth and power. He also wins the hand of a sultan's beautiful daughter.

The Thousand and One Nights has about 200 stories and took me forever to read. I was sad, though, when the stories finally ended. No other book could provide more reading enjoyment.

15. Which of these is a *fact* about *The Thousand and One Nights?*
    Ⓐ It is the most exciting book ever written.
    Ⓑ No other book could provide more reading enjoyment.
    Ⓒ It took forever to read.
    Ⓓ It is a collection of ancient folktales.

16. Which of these expresses an *opinion?*
    Ⓐ "Aladdin" is the best story in *The Thousand and One Nights.*
    Ⓑ Scheherazade wove tales to save her life.
    Ⓒ "Sinbad the Sailor" is one tale from *The Thousand and One Nights.*
    Ⓓ *The Thousand and One Nights* has humor, adventure, and romance.

Read this journal entry from a member of a cruise ship. Then answer questions about the journal entry. Choose the best answer for Numbers 1 through 6.

Monday, December 5

The *Sea Rover* has just left the island of Bermuda. It is traveling south to Puerto Rico. On Friday, the ship will turn west and head back to Miami. This route takes us through the most dreaded area in the Atlantic Ocean—the Bermuda Triangle!

The Bermuda Triangle got its name after an event that occurred in 1945. On December 5, five United States Navy planes vanished while flying over the region. No one knows how or why this happened. After one of the largest searches in history, no wreckage was ever found—not until May 1991, that is. Finally, the five missing planes were found just 10 miles off the Florida coast.

Since 1945, more than one hundred ships and planes are believed to have vanished in the Bermuda Triangle. For this reason, the region is also known as the Devil's Triangle, Atlantic's Graveyard, and the Twilight Zone.

Books and TV shows have provided many reasons for the mysterious disappearances. Some people blame undersea earthquakes. They say that the earthquakes churned up gargantuan waves that swallowed up the vessels. Others believe that the missing boats and planes entered time warps and were sent into the past or the future. A few people claim that aliens were to blame for the missing vessels.

Accidents can happen at sea. Most disappearances were probably caused by bad weather, broken equipment, or human error. There are just as many losses in other parts of the ocean as in the Bermuda Triangle. The ocean is vast and deep. It's not surprising some vessels are never found.

Finding Word Meaning in Context

1. In the first paragraph, the name *Sea Rover* probably means
    - Ⓐ "a sea dog or sailor."
    - Ⓑ "a ship that roams the sea."
    - Ⓒ "a boat that is propelled by oars."
    - Ⓓ "a ship that is lost at sea."

Finding Word Meaning in Context

2. In paragraph 4, the best meaning of *gargantuan* is
    - Ⓐ "tiny."
    - Ⓑ "huge."
    - Ⓒ "smooth."
    - Ⓓ "graceful."

Drawing Conclusions and Making Inferences

3. There is enough information in the journal entry to show that
    - Ⓐ most disappearances in the Bermuda Triangle can be explained.
    - Ⓑ there is no such thing as the Bermuda Triangle.
    - Ⓒ most pilots and ship captains avoid the Bermuda Triangle.
    - Ⓓ crossing the ocean by ship or boat is perfectly safe.

Drawing Conclusions and Making Inferences

4. From the journal entry, you can figure out that the cruise-ship member
    - Ⓐ doesn't believe that the disappearances were ordinary accidents.
    - Ⓑ likes to solve mysteries.
    - Ⓒ is trying to understand the mystery of the Bermuda Triangle.
    - Ⓓ is thrilled to be traveling through the Bermuda Triangle.

Distinguishing Between Fact and Opinion

5. Which of these is an *opinion* from the journal entry?
    - Ⓐ Books provide many reasons for the disappearances.
    - Ⓑ Accidents can happen at sea.
    - Ⓒ In 1945, five navy planes were lost in the Bermuda Triangle.
    - Ⓓ The Bermuda Triangle is the most dreaded area in the Atlantic Ocean.

Distinguishing Between Fact and Opinion

6. Which of these is a *fact*?
    - Ⓐ More should be done to understand the Bermuda Triangle.
    - Ⓑ Undersea earthquakes are amazing events.
    - Ⓒ The Bermuda Triangle is also called Atlantic's Graveyard.
    - Ⓓ Only foolish people believe in time warps.

Read this short biography of a famous president. Then answer questions about the biography. Choose the best answer for Numbers 7 through 12.

Did you know that the popular teddy bear was named for President Theodore ("Teddy") Roosevelt? He was the 26th president of the United States. It is said that, while hunting in Mississippi, a small bear cub was brought to President Roosevelt to shoot. But he refused. He believed that the animal did not have a chance to defend itself. The story of his tender deed quickly spread, and soon the country was flooded with stuffed bear cubs, or teddy bears.

Roosevelt was born in 1858 to a wealthy family from New York City. As a child, he was often sick. As he grew, he made himself stronger by exercising. In time, Roosevelt became quite a sportsman. He was a good boxer, horseman, rower, tennis player, and hunter.

Roosevelt had many careers. He was a writer, a rancher, and a lawyer. In politics, he served as a police commissioner, a governor, a vice president, and, of course, president. He was also a national war hero. In 1898, Roosevelt served as a colonel in the Spanish-American War. The United States fought in this war to help Cuba win its freedom from Spain. Roosevelt formed a regiment of horsemen known as the Rough Riders. His bravery during battle led to his rise in politics. In 1898, he was elected governor of New York. In March 1901, he became vice president to President William McKinley. When McKinley was killed six months later, Roosevelt became president. He was the youngest man ever to become president. He was only 42.

President Roosevelt never rested. He helped to pass important laws. He forced companies to give workers higher wages and improve working conditions. He took steps to protect our country's wilderness. He set aside tracts of land as national parks and forests. He supported the building of the Panama Canal to make it easier for ships to travel between the Atlantic and the Pacific. In 1906, he won the Nobel Peace Prize for helping to end a war between Russia and Japan. He was the first American president to win a Nobel Prize. He was also the first president to ride in a car, fly in an airplane, and travel in a submarine.

Despite his busy schedule, Roosevelt always made time for his six children. He told them stories and played games. Together, they wrestled, played hide-and-seek, and had wild pillow fights.

Theodore Roosevelt died in 1919 at age 60. But every American still remembers the man with the big heart. A likeness of his face is carved at Mount Rushmore, in South Dakota.

Finding Word Meaning in Context

7. In paragraph 3, *regiment* means
   - Ⓐ "a daily diet."
   - Ⓑ "a special routine."
   - Ⓒ "a military unit."
   - Ⓓ "to put in order."

Drawing Conclusions and Making Inferences

10. From the biography, you can tell that Roosevelt
    - Ⓐ loved the West.
    - Ⓑ had a great sense of humor.
    - Ⓒ owned many teddy bears.
    - Ⓓ had a lot of energy.

Finding Word Meaning in Context

8. In paragraph 4, you can tell that the word *tracts* means
   - Ⓐ "paths or trails."
   - Ⓑ "where trains run."
   - Ⓒ "small spaces."
   - Ⓓ "large areas."

Distinguishing Between Fact and Opinion

11. Which of these is an *opinion* from the biography?
    - Ⓐ Roosevelt was the first president to win a Nobel Prize.
    - Ⓑ Roosevelt had many careers.
    - Ⓒ Roosevelt never rested.
    - Ⓓ Roosevelt was the youngest person to become president.

Drawing Conclusions and Making Inferences

9. There is enough information in the biography to show that Roosevelt
   - Ⓐ was an adventurous man.
   - Ⓑ was a stern colonel.
   - Ⓒ was known to behave foolishly.
   - Ⓓ was a devoted husband.

Distinguishing Between Fact and Opinion

12. Which of these is a *fact*?
    - Ⓐ Everyone has heard of teddy bears.
    - Ⓑ The teddy bear was named for "Teddy" Roosevelt.
    - Ⓒ Roosevelt was the most wonderful and caring of fathers.
    - Ⓓ All Americans admired Roosevelt.

IDENTIFYING AUTHOR'S PURPOSE

PART ONE: Think About the Strategy

What Is Author's Purpose?

Authors always write for a reason. Everything you read has a purpose. An author's purpose is either to describe, to entertain, to explain, or to persuade.

Write what you think the author's purpose is for writing each of the following. Tell if the author's purpose is to describe, to entertain, to explain, or to persuade.

1 A newspaper article

The author's purpose is to _____ .

2 A tall tale about a silly character

The author's purpose is to _____ .

3 An advertisement

The author's purpose is to _____ .

4 A paragraph about a sunset

The author's purpose is to _____ .

Work with a Partner

- Take turns talking about some of the things you see on TV. Think about things such as comedy shows, science shows, commercials, and so on.
- Together, see if you can identify the author's purpose for what you see.

How Do You Find Author's Purpose?

Every reading passage is written for a reason. When you read, ask yourself, "What does the author want me to know?" Your answer will help you figure out the author's purpose.

Read this passage about a war among animals. See if you can figure out the author's purpose for writing the passage.

> **The Birds, the Beasts, and the Bat**
> Long ago, the birds waged a war against the other animals. Bat, an animal that flies like a bird, sensed that he had an advantage. So he continuously changed sides in the war to stay on the winning side. When peace was restored, all the birds and beasts shunned him. They said, "You're a coward, for you didn't have the courage to commit to a side. You are banned from daylight and must fly alone at night."

1. Think about what the author wants you to know.

   Let's narrow down the choices by using the chart below.

2. Check "yes" or "no" for each choice. You can check "yes" only once in this chart.

	Yes	No	
Does the passage mostly give details about a particular person, place, or thing?			Describe
Does the passage tell a humorous story or teach a lesson?			Entertain
Does the passage give facts about something or tell how to do something?			Explain
Does the passage try to get you to do or buy something?			Persuade

3. Write the choice that has a check mark for "yes."

_____

WHAT TO KNOW

All authors write for a reason. The reason an author writes something is called the author's purpose. When you figure out why a reading passage was written, you are **identifying the author's purpose**. Authors write for one of four reasons— to describe, to entertain, to explain, or to persuade.

- If a reading passage contains many details about a person, place, or thing, the author's purpose is to **describe**.

- If a reading passage is enjoyable to read, tells a personal story, or uses a story to teach a lesson, the author's purpose is to **entertain**.

- If a reading passage provides facts about a particular subject or tells readers how to do something, the author's purpose is to **explain**.

- If a reading passage tries to get readers to do something, buy something, or believe something, the author's purpose is to **persuade**.

Read this retelling of a fable. As you read, think about why the fable was written.

One day, a frog was hopping around the farm on which he lived. On this day, he decided to explore the barn where all the cows were kept. Being that this particular frog was as curious as he was careless, he jumped into a pail half-filled with milk.

The frog tried with all of his might to hop out of the pail, but the sides were much too high. Now, this particular frog was also as stubborn as he was spirited. So he decided that he was not going to give up without a fight.

The frog swam about in the milk, kicking and squirming all the while, until at last all of his churning turned the milk into butter. The frog climbed on top of the solid chunk of butter and easily hopped out of the pail.

Moral: *Where there's a will, there's a way.*

The author probably wrote this fable to make readers laugh or smile. The author's purpose is to entertain readers with a fable that teaches a lesson.

Read this newspaper article written about Thanksgiving Day. As you read, try to figure out the author's purpose for writing the article. Then answer the questions.

Thanksgiving Myths

by I. M. Agobbler

For more than one hundred years, Thanksgiving Day has been celebrated in November. No one really knows, though, when the first Thanksgiving took place. Records show only that it occurred sometime in the autumn of 1621. The early Thanksgivings didn't occur each year. And they didn't always happen in the fall. In 1623, for example, Thanksgiving was celebrated in July.

Today, turkey is the most popular choice for Thanksgiving dinner. However, it was unlikely that turkey was served at the first Thanksgiving. In fact, there probably wasn't a turkey within miles of the feast. The Pilgrims and their Native American guests fed mostly on deer, duck, goose, and seafood. They also ate corn bread, vegetables, and fruits.

For its first two hundred years, Thanksgiving was popular mainly with New Englanders. In 1827, Sarah Josepha Hale began a campaign to make Thanksgiving a national holiday. Finally, in 1863, President Lincoln set aside the last Thursday of November as the official holiday.

In 1939, President Roosevelt moved Thanksgiving to the third Thursday of November. The change occurred so that there would be more shopping days for the December holidays. Many Americans, though, didn't like the change. So, in 1941, Congress declared that Thanksgiving Day would fall on the fourth Thursday of November. And so it has ever since.

1. The author wrote the article mainly to
   Ⓐ explain the facts about Thanksgiving.
   Ⓑ describe the first Thanksgiving meal.
   Ⓒ convince readers not to eat turkey on Thanksgiving.
   Ⓓ entertain readers with an amusing story about Thanksgiving mistakes.

2. You know your answer to question 1 is correct because the article mainly
   Ⓐ contains many details that describe a person, place, or thing.
   Ⓑ provides lots of facts and information about something.
   Ⓒ tries to convince readers of something.
   Ⓓ tells an enjoyable story.

 Work with a Partner

- Talk about your answers to the questions.
- Tell why you chose your answers.
- Then talk about what you have learned so far about identifying author's purpose.

REVIEW

Authors write to describe, to entertain, to explain, or to persuade.

- As you read, ask yourself, "Does the reading passage contain many details that describe a person, place, or thing?" If so, the author's purpose is to describe.

- As you read, ask yourself, "Does the reading passage tell an enjoyable or a personal story? Does the author use a story to teach a lesson?" If so, the author's purpose is to entertain.

- As you read, ask yourself, "Does the reading passage provide facts about a particular subject? Does the passage tell me how to do something?" If so, the author's purpose is to explain.

- As you read, ask yourself, "Does the reading passage try to convince me to do something, buy something, or believe something?" If so, the author's purpose is to persuade.

Read these instructions for an art project. As you read, ask yourself, "Why did the author probably write these instructions?" Then answer the questions.

Pendulum Art

If you suspend an object and give it a push, it will move back and forth at a regular rate. In science, this action is called *simple harmonic motion.* You can use this action to create art. The materials you will need are a bowl, a sheet of construction paper, a pencil, scissors, tape, a small plastic funnel, string, a large sheet of black paper, and a cup of salt.

1. Trace the rim of the bowl on the construction paper and cut out the circle. Next, cut away a quarter of the circle. Then pull the sides of the circle together until they form a cone. Tape the cone together, but leave a small hole at the tip. Place the cone into the funnel.
2. Tie some string around the lip of the funnel. Use more string to suspend the funnel a few inches above a table or a counter surface.
3. Place the black paper under the funnel.
4. Block the funnel's tip with a finger, and pour in the salt.
5. Remove your finger, and push the funnel gently to make it swing. The salt will form a pattern on the black paper.

3. The author wrote the instructions mainly to
   Ⓐ persuade readers to study simple harmonic motion.
   Ⓑ describe what a pendulum is.
   Ⓒ explain how to do an art project.
   Ⓓ entertain readers with a story about a pendulum.

4. You know your answer to question 3 is correct because the instructions mainly
   Ⓐ describe in detail a person, place, or thing.
   Ⓑ provide facts or tell readers how to do something.
   Ⓒ try to convince readers of something.
   Ⓓ tell an enjoyable story.

Which Answer Is Correct and Why?

Look at the answer choices for each question.
Read why each answer choice is correct or not correct.

3. The author wrote the instructions mainly to

Ⓐ **persuade readers to study simple harmonic motion.**

This answer is not correct because the instructions do not contain many reasons that try to convince readers they should study simple harmonic motion.

Ⓑ **describe what a pendulum is.**

This answer is not correct because the instructions do not contain many details that describe a pendulum. The instructions mainly contain information about how to create a pendulum.

● **explain how to do an art project.**

This answer is correct because the instructions provide information that tells readers how to make pendulum art.

Ⓓ **entertain readers with a story about a pendulum.**

This answer is not correct because the instructions do not tell an interesting story or try to make readers laugh.

4. You know your answer to question 3 is correct because the instructions mainly

Ⓐ **describe in detail a person, place, or thing.**

This answer is not correct because the instructions do not contain many details that describe a particular person, place, or thing.

● **provide facts or tell readers how to do something.**

This answer is correct because the instructions do provide information that explains how to create pendulum art.

Ⓒ **try to convince readers of something.**

This answer is not correct because the instructions do not try to convince readers to do something, buy something, or believe something.

Ⓓ **tell an enjoyable story.**

This answer is not correct because the instructions do not tell an interesting story.

MORE TO KNOW	• Each paragraph in a reading selection can have its own purpose. As you read each paragraph, ask yourself, "Why was this particular paragraph written? Was the author's purpose to describe, to entertain, to explain, or to persuade?" • The entire reading passage has one main purpose. After you have finished reading the passage, ask yourself, "Why was this passage mainly written? What did the author probably want readers to know?"

Read this article about wild animals as pets. Then answer the questions.

Many people are tempted to keep wild animals as pets. Some think fox cubs are great to cuddle. Some think that monkeys are fun to train. And others think that having exotic snakes will impress their friends. But keeping wild animals as pets is not a good idea.

Wild animals often grow to be stronger and more dangerous than their owners expected. These animals have natural instincts that cause them to change as they grow. Young animals can grow to be large animals that bite, scratch, and even attack humans. Owners often abandon their pets when this happens.

Many wild animals carry diseases that are harmful to people. It's not only large animals that carry harmful germs. Small animals, such as rabbits, chicks, and mice, spread them, too. So do many kinds of reptiles. Turtles less than four inches long can make children very sick.

It's not fair to keep wild animals in cages or backyards. They often become sick or die because their owners don't care for them properly. Admire wild animals in their natural habitat, and get a dog or cat as a pet.

5. The author's main purpose in the first paragraph is to
   Ⓐ describe why fox cubs make good pets.
   Ⓑ explain why people keep wild animals as pets.
   Ⓒ entertain readers with a personal story.
   Ⓓ persuade readers to raise exotic snakes.

6. The author's main purpose in paragraph 2 is to
   Ⓐ describe how wild animals can change.
   Ⓑ explain why wild animals are so strong.
   Ⓒ entertain readers with an animal riddle.
   Ⓓ persuade readers not to abandon pets.

7. The author's main purpose in paragraph 3 is to
   Ⓐ describe the diseases that are carried by wild animals.
   Ⓑ explain that wild animals carry diseases.
   Ⓒ entertain readers with a silly pet story.
   Ⓓ persuade readers that animals are safe.

8. The article was mainly written to
   Ⓐ describe how to care for wild animals.
   Ⓑ explain the difference between wild animals and pets.
   Ⓒ entertain readers with a fun story.
   Ⓓ persuade readers not to keep wild animals as pets.

Read this passage about the unicorn. Then answer the questions.

People from all parts of the world have told and written about the unicorn for thousands of years. The first description of this legendary creature appeared about 400 B.C. A Greek physician named Ctesias had traveled to ancient Persia, where he heard many marvelous tales. Ctesias wrote that in India, there were unusual wild donkeys. They had a white body, dark-red head, and a pointed horn on the forehead. The horn was about 20 inches long. It was white at the base, black in the middle, and bright red at the tip.

Over time, the image of the unicorn slowly changed. Eventually, the unicorn came to be a pure-white creature. It had the body and head of a small horse, the legs of a deer, and the tail of a lion. On its forehead was a magnificent twisted horn.

During the Middle Ages, people believed that the unicorn's horn had special powers. It could guard against poison, illness, and evil. People paid a lot of money for the horns. Most of these horns, though, were probably the tusks of narwhals. The narwhal is a small Arctic whale that has a spiral tusk growing from its snout.

Today, common belief is that there are no more unicorns on earth. Some people claim that unicorns were hunted until there were none left. Other people insist that unicorns never existed. Real or not, the legend of the extraordinary unicorn lives on.

9. The author wrote the first paragraph mainly to
   Ⓐ explain why unicorns have horns.
   Ⓑ persuade readers to visit Persia.
   Ⓒ describe what the first unicorns were said to have looked like.
   Ⓓ entertain readers with a fanciful legend about unicorns.

10. The author wrote paragraph 3 mainly to
   Ⓐ persuade readers to learn more about the Middle Ages.
   Ⓑ explain that unicorn horns were probably narwhal tusks.
   Ⓒ describe what a narwhal looks like.
   Ⓓ entertain readers with a silly comparison.

11. The author wrote the last paragraph mainly to
   Ⓐ explain why unicorns disappeared.
   Ⓑ convince readers that the unicorn— real or not—is special.
   Ⓒ amuse readers with a riddle about an extraordinary animal.
   Ⓓ describe an imaginary creature.

12. The passage was written mainly to
   Ⓐ describe an unusual creature.
   Ⓑ explain why the unicorn is legendary.
   Ⓒ entertain readers with a story about a magnificent beast.
   Ⓓ persuade readers that the unicorn had special powers.

TEST TIPS

- A test question about identifying the author's purpose may ask you why an author probably wrote a particular reading passage. This kind of question is asking about the purpose of the entire reading passage.

- A test question about identifying the author's purpose may ask why a particular paragraph was written. This kind of question is asking about only one part of the reading passage.

- A test question about identifying the author's purpose may ask what you think the author wants readers to know. To help you answer, think about why the author probably wrote the reading passage.

Read this clever poem. Then answer questions about the poem. Choose the best answer for Numbers 13 and 14.

Stately Verse

If Mary goes far out to sea,
    By wayward breezes fanned,
I'd like to know—can you tell me?—
    Just where would Maryland?

If Tenny went high up in the air
    And looked o'er land and lea,
Looked here and there and everywhere,
    Pray what would Tennessee?

I looked out of the window and
    Saw Orry on the lawn;
He's not there now, and who can tell
    Just where has Oregon?

Two girls were quarreling one day
    With garden tools, and so
I said, "My dears, let Mary rake
    And just let Idaho."

A friend of mine lived in a flat
    With half a dozen boys;
When he fell ill I asked him why.
    He said: "I'm Illinois."

An English lady had a steed.
    She called him Ighland Bay.
She rode for exercise, and thus
    Rhode Island every day.

                                    Anonymous

13. The author wrote the poem mainly to
Ⓐ explain how some states got their names.
Ⓑ describe some girls and boys.
Ⓒ convince readers to learn the names of all the states.
Ⓓ entertain readers with humorous word play.

14. The author probably wants readers to know that
Ⓐ silly stories can be made out of the names of some states.
Ⓑ some states are named after people.
Ⓒ they can use their own names to write a poem about state names.
Ⓓ most state names have unusual origins.

Read this invitation sent to students in Bell County. Then answer questions about the invitation. Choose the best answer for Numbers 15 and 16.

Are you someone with big ideas?
Do you want to be known as someone who shaped the future?
If so, then here's an opportunity that might interest you.

WHAT: The Spirit of Invention Science Fair
WHO: Any student in grades 5 through 12 from the Bell County schools
WHEN: Saturday, April 7
- Set up: 9:00 A.M.
- Judging: 11:00 A.M.
- Public viewing: 1:00–3:00 P.M.
WHERE: The George Washington Carver Auditorium, St. Louis, Missouri
HOW:
1. Research the invention you have in mind. (Simple inventions can also be a success.)
2. Design a model of the invention.
3. Create posters and write a journal describing the invention.
4. Be prepared to explain to judges why your invention is important to society.
WHY: Top inventions at each grade level win a cash prize. The grand-prize winner wins the services of a patent attorney in the hopes of someday selling the invention in the marketplace.

15. The author uses an invitation format mainly to
    Ⓐ persuade students to design only simple inventions.
    Ⓑ describe what a successful invention is.
    Ⓒ explain all the facts students need to know about a science fair.
    Ⓓ entertain readers with a tale about a great inventor.

16. What is the main purpose of the "why" part of the invitation?
    Ⓐ to convince students to enter the science fair
    Ⓑ to describe what services a patent attorney provides
    Ⓒ to explain that everyone wins a prize
    Ⓓ to delight readers with information about prizes

INTERPRETING FIGURATIVE LANGUAGE

PART ONE: Think About the Strategy

What Is Figurative Language?

Has anyone ever told you that you were tooting your own horn? If so, that person thought you were bragging about something. Have you ever bent over backwards to help someone? If so, you tried very hard to help the person. Figurative language is the use of words in a way that is different from what the words usually mean.

1 Read this sentence.

> Jacob's new invention will amaze you!

2 Now read this next sentence. It uses different words, but it has the same meaning as the first sentence.

> Jacob's new invention will knock your socks off!

3 Write which sentence is more interesting, the first one or the second one. Tell why you think this is so.

_____

_____

_____

Work with a Partner

- Talk about some of the words you have used or heard that have a meaning different from their usual meaning. For example, a friend might tell you that she is "playing it by ear." Your friend is telling you that she is waiting to see what happens before deciding what to do.

- See how many examples of figurative language you can think of.

How Do You Understand Figurative Language?

Sometimes you can use word meaning in context to help you understand figurative language. Look for clues in a reading passage to help you figure out what new meaning the words could have. Clues might be in the sentence where the words are found. They may also be in the sentence just before or just after the one in which the words are found.

Read this passage about Hector. See if you can figure out what the phrase *spread himself too thin* **means.**

> When school started in the fall, Hector signed up for as many school activities as he could. He was working on the school newspaper, acting in the drama club, and playing in the marching band. Hector soon realized that he couldn't do all of his schoolwork and keep up with all of his activities. He had spread himself too thin. Hector would have to give some things up.

1. Let's narrow down the clues to figure out what the phrase *spread himself too thin* means.

   Look at the chart below. It shows three sentences: the one that comes before the phrase *spread himself too thin*, the one that contains the phrase *spread himself too thin*, and the one that comes after the phrase *spread himself too thin*.

   Look carefully at the sentences that come before and after the phrase *spread himself too thin*.

Hector soon realized that he couldn't do all of his schoolwork and keep up with all of his activities.	He had spread himself too thin.	Hector would have to give some things up.
Before		After

2. Now think about what the clues in the sentences tell you:

   Hector couldn't keep up with all of his schoolwork and all of his activities.
   Hector didn't have enough time in his schedule to do everything he wanted.
   Hector was going to have to give some things up.

   So the phrase *spread himself too thin* must mean

   _____ .

WHAT TO KNOW

Similes, metaphors, and idioms are types of figurative language. Authors use figurative language to help readers create pictures in their mind. When you understand the meaning of a simile, a metaphor, or an idiom, you are **interpreting figurative language**.

- Look for things that are compared in a reading passage. Try to find examples of similes or metaphors.

- Look for phrases whose words have a meaning different from their usual meaning. Try to find examples of idioms.

- Figurative language usually brings a picture to a reader's mind. Use that picture to help you understand the meaning of the figurative language.

Read this sentence. As you read, think about the two things being compared.

The hour passed as slowly as a turtle crawling in sand.
The two things being compared are an hour and a turtle.
The writer used a **simile** to help readers picture how slowly the hour passed.
A simile uses the word *like* or *as* to compare two different things.

Read this sentence. As you read, think about the two things being compared.

The stars are brilliant diamonds in a black sky.
The two things being compared are stars and diamonds.
The writer used a **metaphor** to help readers picture the sight of the stars.
A metaphor compares two different things but does not use the word *like* or *as*.
A metaphor says that one thing *is* another thing.

Now read this sentence. As you read, think about the meaning of the underlined words.

Manuel and Michael met at camp and really <u>hit it off</u>.
The underlined words mean that the boys quickly became good friends.
The underlined words are an **idiom**.
An idiom is a phrase whose words have a meaning different from their usual meaning.

Read this description of a tall-tale hero. As you read, ask yourself, "What pictures come to mind?" Then answer the questions.

Big Mose

Big Mose was once the bravest fireman in New York City. He was also the biggest and the strongest. He could carry streetcars and swim all the way around Manhattan Island in just six strokes. Mose stood twelve feet tall and wore a stovepipe hat that made him two feet taller. His hands were as large as Virginia hams. He had flaming red hair and eyes that twinkled with mischief. His laughter sounded like the roar of Niagara Falls and caused buildings to shake.

In Mose's day, fire engines looked like big wagons with long handles on the sides. They had a condenser in the middle and a long hose. Firemen would pump water through the condenser into the hose and toward the flames. The old fire machines had no engines or horses to move them along. It took dozens of firemen to pull each machine through the city streets.

Mose had his own fire machine called *Lady Washington*. She was the finest fire machine in the city. Mose loved that "old gal." It made his heart proud to run alongside her.

Mose had a heart of gold and always did his duty. When a fire alarm sounded, he was the first one to arrive at the firehouse and pull on his striped suspenders, bright-red shirt, giant boots, and fire helmet. He walked through flames as if they were made of candlesticks. All kinds of people thanked him for saving their lives. "Just doing my duty," he would always reply.

1. In the first paragraph, Mose's laughter is compared to
   (A) a ringing fire alarm.
   (B) an old fire machine.
   (C) the sound of falling bricks.
   (D) the roar of Niagara Falls.

2. In the last paragraph, the phrase *had a heart of gold* means that Mose was
   (A) interested in being rich.
   (B) generous and friendly.
   (C) selfish and unkind.
   (D) wealthy in many ways.

Work with a Partner

- Talk about your answers to the questions.
- Tell why you chose your answers.
- Then talk about what you have learned so far about interpreting figurative language.

REVIEW

Similes, metaphors, and idioms are types of figurative language. Authors use figurative language to help readers create pictures in their mind.

- Look for things that are compared in a reading passage. See if the word *like* or *as* is used, or if a sentence says that one thing is another thing.

- Look for phrases whose words have a meaning different from their usual meaning.

- Think about any pictures that come to mind as you read. Use these pictures to help you understand what is being described.

Read this fable from Aesop. As you read, look for things that are compared. Also look for words that have a meaning different from their usual meaning. Then answer the questions.

The Miser

A miser sold everything he had for a bag of gold coins. He melted down the gold into a single lump, which he buried secretly in a field. Every day, he went to look at the spot. Sometimes, he would spend long hours gloating over his treasure. A man noticed the miser's frequent visits to the field and one day discovered his secret. That night, the man waited for just the right moment, and then he dug up the gold and carried it away.

The next day, the miser visited the place as usual. Finding his treasure gone, his face darkened like a cloud. Then he began tearing out his hair and groaning over his loss. One of his neighbors saw him in this condition and asked the miser what his trouble was. The miser told the man of his misfortune.

"Don't take it to heart, my friend," the man replied. "Put a brick into the hole and take a look at it every day. You won't be any worse off than before, for even when you had your gold, it was of no use to you."

3. In the second paragraph, the miser's face is compared to
   Ⓐ a lump of gold.
   Ⓑ a brick.
   Ⓒ a cloud.
   Ⓓ a tornado.

4. In the last paragraph, the phrase *take it to heart* means
   Ⓐ "hold something against the heart."
   Ⓑ "take something seriously."
   Ⓒ "act stingy with money."
   Ⓓ "enjoy something too much."

Which Answer Is Correct and Why?

Look at the answer choices for each question.
Read why each answer choice is correct or not correct.

3. In the last paragraph, the miser's face is compared to

   Ⓐ a lump of gold.

   This answer is not correct because there is no comparison between the miser's face and the lump of gold he treasures.

   Ⓑ a brick.

   This answer is not correct because there is no comparison between the miser's face and the brick that the neighbor mentions.

   ⬤ a cloud.

   This answer is correct because the paragraph states that the miser's face *"darkened like a cloud."* The word *like* signals that two things are being compared in a simile.

   Ⓓ a tornado.

   This answer is not correct because the word *tornado* is not used in the fable.

4. In the last paragraph, the phrase *take it to heart* means

   Ⓐ "hold something against the heart."

   This answer is not correct because there are no details in the fable to hint at this meaning of the phrase. The miser's treasure is gone; it would be impossible for him to hold it against his heart.

   ⬤ "take something seriously."

   This answer is correct because the details in the fable suggest that the miser was taking the loss of his treasure very seriously. His face darkened like a cloud, he tore out his hair, and he groaned over his misfortune.

   Ⓒ "act stingy with money."

   This answer is not correct because there are no details in the paragraph to hint at this meaning. The miser cannot be stingy with something he no longer has.

   Ⓓ "enjoy something too much."

   This answer is not correct because there are no details in the fable to hint at this meaning. The miser is upset that he lost his gold; therefore, he could not be enjoying anything at the moment.

| MORE TO KNOW | • Think about the things being compared in a simile or metaphor. Ask yourself, "What do the two things have in common?" This will help you create pictures in your mind.
• Look at the sentences near an idiom. You might find context clues to help you figure out its meaning. |

Read this radio interview. Then answer the questions.

Interviewer: We'd like to welcome the director Dred Fuller to our show. Mr. Fuller is the Steven Spielberg of horror films. Tell us, Dred, how did you become so interested in monsters?

Dred Fuller: Everyone is fascinated by monsters, not just me. For some strange reason, we enjoy things that scare the daylights out of us.

Interviewer: Let's talk about your latest film, *The Werewolf of Los Angeles*. Where did you get the idea for this movie?

Dred Fuller: When I was a kid, I saw the classic film *The Wolf Man*. This movie blew my mind. The story is about a young man who got bitten by a werewolf. Afterwards, whenever there was a full moon, the man would turn into a werewolf and terrorize innocent people. The werewolf was a hairy two-legged creature with fangs as sharp as daggers. Each time it appeared on screen, I screamed as loud as the beast.

Interviewer: What is your next project?

Dred Fuller: I'm making a new movie version of the novel *Frankenstein,* by Mary Shelley. My film will be called *Frankly Frankenstein.*

5. The interviewer compares Dred Fuller to
   Ⓐ the Wolf Man.
   Ⓑ Frankenstein.
   Ⓒ Steven Spielberg.
   Ⓓ Mary Shelley.

6. The phrase *scare the daylights out of* means
   Ⓐ "make someone afraid of the dark."
   Ⓑ "frighten someone a lot."
   Ⓒ "shut off the lights."
   Ⓓ "turn day into night."

7. What does *blew my mind* mean?
   Ⓐ "caused amazement"
   Ⓑ "prevented something"
   Ⓒ "caused hatred"
   Ⓓ "have a headache"

8. The sharpness of the werewolf's fangs is compared to that of
   Ⓐ knives.   Ⓒ needles.
   Ⓑ razors.   Ⓓ daggers.

Read this amusing poem. Then answer the questions.

Uncle Setchell
by stevan-adele Morley and Robert G. Forest

Uncle Setchell has hair that sticks out like thatch,
White as raw turnip from a vegetable patch.
He combs it in haste, using fingers for tines,
And pulls at the snarls entangled like vines.
He's a grizzly brown bear with leatherhide skin
And porcupine whiskers that blanket his chin.
A man of good humor, blue eyes all aglow,
He greets each new day with a thunderous "Hello."
His hands are like vises; they're tight in the clutch.
He doesn't speak often and never says much.
He chews on a matchstick at the side of his mouth
And fishes for hours in the crick to the south.
He favors ol' Gator—he's fond of the hound
That sticks to his side like an oak sticks to ground.
Each Saturday, Aunt Nettie sets out the wood tub
And pleads with her husband to bathe and to scrub.
He scowls and scoffs, and he scolds with disgust,
"Let me outta this tub; I'm beginning to rust!"

9. In the poem, Uncle Setchell's hair is compared to
   Ⓐ sticks.
   Ⓑ porcupine whiskers.
   Ⓒ thatch.
   Ⓓ a vegetable patch.

10. Which two things are compared in the poem?
    Ⓐ brown hair and raw turnips
    Ⓑ snarled hair and tangled vines
    Ⓒ skin and a blanket
    Ⓓ blue eyes and the sky

11. The words *His hands are like vises* mean that Uncle Setchell's hands
    Ⓐ have a strong grip.
    Ⓑ are always closed in a tight fist.
    Ⓒ look like clamping devices.
    Ⓓ snap shut with great force.

12. Which of these is a metaphor?
    Ⓐ He's a man of good humor.
    Ⓑ His hound sticks to his side like an oak sticks to ground.
    Ⓒ He scowls and scoffs, and he scolds with disgust.
    Ⓓ He's a grizzly brown bear.

TEST TIPS

- A test question about interpreting figurative language may ask you about the meaning of a particular simile, metaphor, or idiom.
- A test question about interpreting figurative language may ask you to identify a particular type of figurative language, such as a simile, a metaphor, or an idiom.

Read this article about a natural wonder. Then answer questions about the article. Choose the best answer for Numbers 13 and 14.

An Unnatural Natural Wonder

In central Australia, a huge rock rises out of the flat desert. The Aborigines call the rock Uluru. The name means "great pebble." From a distance, the rock looks like a giant pebble sitting on a level plain. Uluru, which is also called Ayers Rock, is visible from more than 50 miles away. It is the largest single rock in the world. The rock is about 1.5 miles long and a mile wide. It stands about as tall as the Empire State Building in New York. The rock rises 1,143 feet high above the desert floor. However, there may be twice as much rock below the ground as above it.

Uluru is made of red sandstone. The rock was formed under the sea about 600 million years ago. Earth movements pushed it above sea level and tilted it. The rock appears to change color as the sun moves across the sky. At dawn, Uluru is a bright red ball of fire. Later in the day, it turns a deep orange yellow. Sometimes, it is violet.

Aborigines know Uluru as "the place where the wind moans between sunset and dawn." The desert winds blow strongly at the top of the rock. Scientists believe that wind erosion continues to change the rock's surface. The Aborigines, though, believe that Uluru does not change. They and their ancestors have lived around Uluru for 10,000 years and see it as a sacred place. The Aborigines believe that their ancestors made the rock and the land around it. The ancestors had great adventures that, once and for all, changed the flat earth. A valley near Uluru is the path that one ancestor walked. Scratches in Uluru are spear marks from a great battle. A hole shows where an ancestor sat to rest. And a nearby mountain is an ancestor who has fallen asleep.

Ayers Rock in Central Australia

13. In the first paragraph, Uluru's size is compared to
   Ⓐ a level plain.
   Ⓑ the Empire State Building.
   Ⓒ a bright red ball of fire.
   Ⓓ the setting sun.

14. Which of these is a simile?
   Ⓐ At dawn, Uluru is a bright red ball of fire.
   Ⓑ From a distance, the rock looks like a giant pebble.
   Ⓒ Uluru is the place where the wind moans.
   Ⓓ A nearby mountain is an ancestor who has fallen asleep.

Read this Norse myth. Then answer questions about the myth. Choose the best answer for Numbers 15 and 16.

How Thor Lost His Hammer

Many of our days of the week are named after Norse gods and goddesses. For example, Thursday is named for Thor, the god of thunder.

Thor was the oldest son of Odin, king of all the gods. Thor was a large and powerful man. His temper was as mighty as his strength. Sometimes, his fury was so wild that sparks flew from his red beard and his eyes burned as red as embers. Thor rode in a chariot drawn by two goats, and he carried a magic hammer called Mjolnir, or Thunderbolt. Whenever Thor swung his hammer, lightning flashed in the sky. Thor used Mjolnir to protect the gods against the forces of evil. The hammer crushed whatever it hit. It never missed its target and always flew back to Thor's hand.

One night while Thor slept, Thrym, who was king of all the giants, stole Thor's hammer. Thrym then buried the hammer eight miles underground. He refused to give it back unless Freya, the goddess of beauty, became his wife.

Freya threw a fit when she heard about Thrym's command. She refused to have a hideous giant for a husband. At last, it was decided that Thor must disguise himself as the bride and go to Thrym. Loki, the mischief maker, would dress as a maid and accompany him.

When the two arrived in the world of the giants, they saw that Thrym had prepared a wedding feast. As soon as everyone was seated at the table, "Freya" began devouring great quantities of food.

"Never have I seen a bride eat more!" Thrym exclaimed.

"She hasn't eaten for eight days," Loki explained. "She has been too excited about meeting you."

Thrym then lifted up his bride's veil to kiss her. But when his eyes met hers, he screamed. "Why do Freya's eyes burn like fire?" he cried.

"Her eyes burn because she has not slept for eight nights," said Loki.

"Very well then," said Thrym. "Bring forth Thor's hammer, and let us make our marriage vows."

As soon as the hammer was placed in the bride's lap, Thor stood up and began swinging. The hammer killed Thrym and then one giant after another. Afterward, Thor and Loki jumped into the chariot and carried Thor's hammer back to the land of the gods.

15. In paragraph 2, Thor's eyes are compared to

Ⓐ lightning.

Ⓑ sparks.

Ⓒ red embers.

Ⓓ the sky.

16. In paragraph 4, *threw a fit* means

Ⓐ "got confused."

Ⓑ "behaved carelessly."

Ⓒ "tossed something into the air."

Ⓓ "became angry."

PART ONE: Think About the Strategy

What Is Summarizing?

A summary is a short statement that tells the main points or important ideas of something you have read or watched, such as a play or a TV show. When you restate the important ideas, you are summarizing.

1 Write the name of a movie or TV show that you watched in the past few weeks.

_____

2 Write three important events from the movie or TV show.

_____

_____

_____

3 Write one sentence that tells how you would answer someone who asked you what the movie or TV show was mostly about. Include information about the important events in your sentence.

_____

_____

_____

Work with a Partner

- Take turns summarizing books, movies, or TV shows.
- Make sure to tell about the most important ideas in one sentence.

How Do You Know What Makes a Good Summary?

A good summary of a reading passage depends on the kind of passage you are reading. If you are reading fiction, usually you will read about a character who has a problem. Your summary should tell about the character, the problem, and the solution. If you are reading nonfiction, your summary should tell about the main idea of the passage as well as the important points contained in the paragraphs.

Read this passage about a boy's visit to a nursing home. Think about what would make a good summary.

> Our class went on a field trip to a nursing home today. We each spent an hour visiting one person. I visited with a sweet older woman named Dorothy. Dorothy told me all about her life. I was surprised to learn that we have a lot in common. She likes vanilla ice cream. She also likes sports, especially baseball. We talked about the Red Sox, her favorite team. The hour went by extremely fast. Dorothy said I could come back and visit anytime. When I do, I think I'll bring my baseball-card collection to show her.

1. Let's narrow down the main idea and the important points in this nonfiction passage.

   Look at the chart below. It shows the main idea and three important points about the main idea.

2. Use the main idea and important points to finish the one-sentence summary of the passage in the box at the bottom.

Main Idea
A boy enjoys his visit with a woman at a nursing home.

Important point
The woman tells the boy all about her life.

Important point
The boy is surprised to learn that they have a lot in common.

Important point
The next time he visits, he will bring his baseball-card collection to show her.

Summary

A boy enjoys his visit to a nursing home where he _____
_____ .

WHAT TO KNOW

A summary is a short statement that tells the main points or important ideas of a reading passage. When you restate the important ideas in a short statement, you are **summarizing**.

- A summary is not stated in a reading passage. To create a summary, you must think about and restate the most important ideas.
- A good summary of fiction tells about the main character, the problem, and the solution.
- A good summary of nonfiction tells about the main idea of the passage, as well as the main ideas contained in the paragraphs.

Read this article about Thomas Jefferson. As you read, think about the most important ideas in the article. Then think about what you might tell someone who asks what the article is about.

Thomas Jefferson was the third president of the United States. He was a great man with many ideas and interests. He helped write the Declaration of Independence. He was also an architect, an inventor, and a musician. Some people believe that he had a brilliant mind.

President John F. Kennedy made a remark once while entertaining a group of Nobel Prize winners. He said, "I think this is the most extraordinary collection of talent and human knowledge that has ever been gathered at the White House, with the possible exception of when Thomas Jefferson dined alone."

The most important ideas in the article are:

Thomas Jefferson was the third president of the United States.

He was a great man with many ideas and interests.

Some people, including another president, believe that he had a brilliant mind.

Here is what you might tell someone who asks what the article is about:

Thomas Jefferson, the third president of the United States, was a brilliant man whom many people admire.

Read this famous American short story. As you read, think about the main character's problem and its solution. Then answer the questions.

In a village at the foot of the Catskill Mountains, there once lived a cheerful but lazy farmer named Rip Van Winkle. He was married to a woman who was always demanding that he do his chores. One day, Rip got tired of being pestered. So he took his dog and gun and climbed up the mountains to hunt.

On the mountainside, Rip met an odd little man who was trying to carry a barrel up the mountain. Rip helped the man bring the barrel to a cave, where he met more little men. The odd hosts kindly offered their guest a drink from the barrel. After two swallows, Rip fell into a deep sleep.

When Rip awoke, there was no sign of the little men. Rip reached for his shiny gun, but a rusted gun lay in its spot instead. He called for his dog, but it never appeared. He was also surprised to find that his joints felt stiff, his clothes were ragged, and he had a long gray beard.

Rip returned to his village and saw it had greatly changed. When he went home, he discovered strangers living there. He learned that his wife had died, his children had grown, and that he, in fact, had been asleep for twenty years.

In time, Rip got used to his new surroundings and enjoyed being the oldest person in the village. Each evening, he sat down at the local inn and told stories. The one he told most, of course, was the one about himself.

1. What is Rip Van Winkle's problem in the story?
   Ⓐ He cannot change his lazy ways.
   Ⓑ His life changes greatly when he falls asleep for twenty years.
   Ⓒ He loses his dog while hunting in the mountains.
   Ⓓ He is forced to help a group of wicked little men.

2. What is the best summary of the story?
   Ⓐ A farmer grows old instantly.
   Ⓑ A farmer tries to help a little man but is tricked into working for him instead.
   Ⓒ A farmer, tricked by a group of little men, returns from a hunting trip to find that his world has changed.
   Ⓓ A farmer learns that he likes to tell stories.

Work with a Partner

- Talk about your answers to the questions.
- Tell why you chose your answers.
- Then talk about what you have learned so far about summarizing.

REVIEW	A summary is a short statement that tells the main points or important ideas of a reading passage. • A good summary of fiction tells about the main character's problem and its solution. • A good summary of nonfiction includes the main ideas of the selection.

Read this article about measurements. As you read, ask yourself, "What does a good summary of nonfiction include?" Then answer the questions.

When Is a Foot Not a Foot?

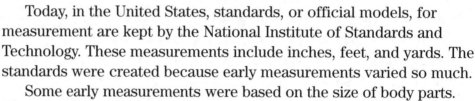

Today, in the United States, standards, or official models, for measurement are kept by the National Institute of Standards and Technology. These measurements include inches, feet, and yards. The standards were created because early measurements varied so much.

Some early measurements were based on the size of body parts. For example, the first inch was the width of a person's thumb. In fact, the English word *inch* probably comes from the Latin word *unica*, which means "thumb." In 1324, King Edward II of England gave this measure a "thumbs down." Thumb widths can vary, and the king wanted a more exact standard that could be used by everyone. So he chose barleycorns as the official standard for inches. By the king's rule, "three grains of barley—placed end to end" equaled an inch.

In ancient times, the foot was the length of an average man's foot. But human feet come in many sizes. Therefore, King Edward II said that a foot should be equal to 36 barleycorns set end to end. This measurement was approximately 12 inches.

The yard was probably first used by merchants to measure cloth. The end of the cloth was held in one outstretched arm while the other arm brought the length of cloth to the nose. You could buy a longer yard from a merchant with a long arm than from a merchant with a short arm.

3. What is the main idea of the article?
   Ⓐ A national institute keeps standards for measurement.
   Ⓑ King Edward II wanted standards for measurement.
   Ⓒ Some early measurements were based on thumb width and foot length.
   Ⓓ Standards were created because early measurements varied so much.

4. What is a good summary of the article?
   Ⓐ King Edward II was the first person to demand more exact standards for measurements.
   Ⓑ Standards for measurements have always varied.
   Ⓒ The standards for measurements became more exact over time.
   Ⓓ Barleycorns were once a standard measure for inches and feet.

Which Answer Is Correct and Why?

**Look at the answer choices for each question.
Read why each answer choice is correct or not correct.**

3. **What is the main idea of the article?**

   Ⓐ **A national institute keeps standards for measurement.**

   This answer is not correct because it does not tell what the article is mostly about. This answer tells only a detail that supports the main idea.

   Ⓑ **King Edward II wanted standards for measurement.**

   This answer is not correct because it does not tell what the article is mostly about. This answer tells only about one detail that supports the main idea.

   Ⓒ **Some early measurements were based on thumb width and foot length.**

   This answer is not correct because it does not tell what the article is mostly about. This answer gives only details that support the main idea.

   ⦿ **Standards were created because early measurements varied so much.**

   This answer is correct because it tells what the article is mostly about. The main idea is stated in the last sentence of the first paragraph. The other facts and details in the article support this main idea.

4. **What is a good summary of the article?**

   Ⓐ **King Edward II was the first person to demand more exact standards for measurements.**

   This answer is not correct because it does not tell enough about the most important ideas in the article, as a good summary of nonfiction should.

   Ⓑ **Standards for measurements have always varied.**

   This answer is not correct because this information is inaccurate. According to the article, standards for measurements once varied but are now kept the same by the National Institute of Standards and Technology.

   ⦿ **The standards for measurements became more exact over time.**

   This answer is correct because it includes the most important ideas in the article. This answer summarizes the main points of what the article is about.

   Ⓓ **Barleycorns were once a standard measure for inches and feet.**

   This answer is not correct because it states only one important detail from the article. A good summary of nonfiction includes the main ideas of the whole selection.

MORE TO KNOW	• A good summary of fiction often tells about the theme, or message, of the story. • A good summary of nonfiction answers *who, what, when, where, why,* and *how* questions.

Read this article about different kinds of vehicles. Then answer the questions.

People today may think that city streets are too crowded with traffic. Yet, city streets have always been filled with traffic. Only the vehicles have changed!

In the 1800s, people got around American cities by taking the horsecar. It was a covered carriage pulled by horses. It ran along rails sunk into the street. The larger horsecars could seat more than a dozen people.

In the 1880s, cities began adopting a new kind of "streetcar." It was not pulled by horses. It was powered by an electric motor. The electricity for the motor came from cables overhead. City streets were soon filled with the screeching of metal wheels against metal tracks. All around was the sound of clanging bells.

In the early 1900s, a strange new vehicle appeared. It had an engine and ran without being connected to cables. People called it a horseless carriage. Before long, these vehicles were everywhere. They were, of course, the first automobiles. Built-up automobiles, called motorbuses, shortly took the place of horsecars. By the 1930s, "buses" had replaced almost all the electric streetcars.

5. What is the article mostly about?
   Ⓐ using buses for city travel
   Ⓑ traffic on city streets
   Ⓒ the disappearance of horsecars
   Ⓓ vehicles that have traveled city streets

6. Which of these were rarely seen on city streets after 1930?
   Ⓐ horseless carriages
   Ⓑ electric streetcars
   Ⓒ buses
   Ⓓ automobiles

7. Why was the automobile important to city travel?
   Ⓐ It was safer than riding a horse.
   Ⓑ It could carry more people.
   Ⓒ It ran without cables.
   Ⓓ It was less noisy.

8. What is a good summary of the article?
   Ⓐ Automobiles and buses replaced horsecars and streetcars during the early 1900s.
   Ⓑ Traffic once crowded city streets.
   Ⓒ Horsecars and streetcars were the first forms of transportation.
   Ⓓ City streets have always been filled with vehicles.

Read this Aztec legend. Then answer the questions.

The Hummingbird Guide

Long ago, the Aztec lived in the dry desert with the cactus. Life was hard. So their god Huitzilopochtli, the hummingbird god, told the Aztec to seek a new home. He also gave the people a new name: Mexica.

The Mexica found a beautiful land of clear sun and bright blue skies. They settled in Aztlan, the "place of the herons." Life seemed good. But all too soon, Huitzilopochtli told the priests that Aztlan was not to be their home. So the priests, carrying statues of Huitzilopochtli on their backs, and the Mexica set out to look for their new home. They wandered year after year. Each time they found a place to settle, they built a temple to their god. But each time, Huitzilopochtli told them to move again. He promised the priests a sign to mark the new home.

The Mexica wandered into the Valley of Mexico. The rich land was crowded with many peoples, and none wanted the Mexica to live there. Finally, an angry group chased them into Lake Texcoco. The Mexica took refuge on an island in the lake. Huitzilopochtli appeared to the priests and ordered them to look among the reeds for the sign. There they saw an eagle with a snake in its mouth standing on a cactus! The grateful Mexica built their city on the island, with a great temple for their god. The city was Tenochtitlán, or "place of the prickly-pear cactus fruit."

9. Who are the main characters in the legend?
   - Ⓐ the Aztec and the Mexica
   - Ⓑ the hummingbird god and the Mexica
   - Ⓒ the eagle and the Mexica
   - Ⓓ the priests and the Mexica

10. What did the Mexica's god do?
    - Ⓐ He ordered the Mexica to build temples to him everywhere they went.
    - Ⓑ He created a great city.
    - Ⓒ He told the Mexica to keep moving until they saw the sign for their home.
    - Ⓓ He forced the Mexica to leave the Valley of Mexico.

11. What did the Mexica do?
    - Ⓐ They built a temple to their god in each place they settled.
    - Ⓑ They looked for a home where life would be easier.
    - Ⓒ They built their final home in Aztlan.
    - Ⓓ They built temples to their gods throughout Mexico.

12. What is a good summary of the legend?
    - Ⓐ The Mexica moved many times until they received a sign that they should make their home in Tenochtitlán.
    - Ⓑ The hummingbird god ordered the Mexica to build him a great temple in their final homeland.
    - Ⓒ The Mexica settled in Aztlan, where they built a temple to their god.
    - Ⓓ The hummingbird god ordered the Mexica to move to an island in Lake Texcoco.

TEST TIPS

- A test question about summarizing may ask you to choose the best summary of a reading passage. When you answer questions about summarizing, first determine if the reading passage is fiction or nonfiction. Then think about what is included in a good summary of fiction or of nonfiction.

- The answer to a test question about summarizing will not be directly stated in the reading passage. You must think about the most important ideas to find the best summary.

Read the lyrics of this song sung by Confederate soldiers. Then answer questions about the lyrics. Choose the best answer for Numbers 13 and 14.

Sitting by the roadside on a summer day,
Chatting with my messmates, passing time away.
Lying in the shadow, underneath the trees,
Goodness how delicious, eating goober peas!

When a horseman passes, the soldiers have a rule:
To cry out at their loudest, "Mister, here's your mule!"
But another pleasure, enchantinger than these,
Is wearing out your grinders eating goober peas!

Just before the battle, the gen'ral hears a row.
He says, "The Yanks are coming; I hear their rifles now."
He turns around in wonder, and what do you think he sees?
The Georgia militia—eating goober peas!

I think my song has lasted almost long enough,
The subject's interesting, but rhymes are mighty rough.
I wish this war was over, when free from rags and fleas,
We'd kiss our wives and sweethearts, and gobble goober peas!

13. The song is mostly about
    Ⓐ eating too many goober peas.
    Ⓑ sitting by the roadside.
    Ⓒ dreaming of eating goober peas.
    Ⓓ passing time between battles.

14. What is a good summary of the song?
    Ⓐ A soldier takes his mind off war by eating goober peas.
    Ⓑ A soldier passes the time between battles by lying in the shade.
    Ⓒ A soldier thinks that goober peas are delicious.
    Ⓓ A soldier takes pleasure in singing to his messmates.

Read this short biography about a leader for women's rights. Then answer questions about the biography. Choose the best answer for Numbers 15 and 16.

In 1820, the year Susan B. Anthony was born, women had almost no rights. They could not speak in public, attend high school or college, or vote. They were also not allowed to own property, run a business, or hold public office.

Susan B. Anthony was born into a Quaker family. Like all Quakers, she grew up believing that men and women are equals. Later, Anthony realized that not everyone shared this belief. As a teacher, she earned three times less than the male teachers.

In 1851, Anthony met Elizabeth Cady Stanton, a leader in the women's rights movement. The two women worked together for more than 50 years. Their biggest goal was for women to be granted the right to vote.

On November 1, 1872, Anthony led 15 women into a voter-registration office in New York. They were asked to leave, but Anthony refused. Instead, she read aloud the Fourteenth and Fifteenth Amendments to the Constitution. They state that all people born in the United States are citizens, and that the right to vote shall not be denied to citizens. Four days later, the women cast their vote for president of the United States.

Three weeks later, all 16 women were arrested. They had broken a federal law. It stated that anyone who votes without having a legal right to do so is guilty of a crime. Only Anthony, however, stood trial. She was found guilty and fined $100. She never paid the fine.

Until her death, at age 86, Anthony devoted all of her time and energy to the women's movement. In the 1890s, four states—Wyoming, Colorado, Idaho, and Utah—finally gave women the right to vote. Then, in 1920 (14 years after Anthony died), the Nineteenth Amendment became law. At last, all women in the United States were granted the right to vote.

In 1979, the United States government issued a new one-dollar coin. This coin had Susan B. Anthony's picture on it. She was the first woman to be so honored.

15. Why was Susan B. Anthony important?
   Ⓐ She was the first woman to have her image on a coin.
   Ⓑ She was a great leader of the women's rights movement.
   Ⓒ She stood trial for her belief in women's right to vote.
   Ⓓ She worked closely with Elizabeth Cady Stanton.

16. Which of these is the best summary of the biography?
   Ⓐ Susan B. Anthony devoted her life to the struggle for women's rights, especially their right to vote.
   Ⓑ Susan B. Anthony worked with Elizabeth Cady Stanton for 50 years to get equal rights for women.
   Ⓒ Susan B. Anthony was a Quaker who believed that men and women are equals.
   Ⓓ Susan B. Anthony did not rest until all women were granted the right to vote.

Read this story adapted from an Indian fable. Then answer questions about the story. Choose the best answer for Numbers 1 through 6.

The Wise Old Goose

A flock of wild geese lived in the high branches of a tree in the forest. One day, the oldest goose looked down at the base of the tree and saw a vine beginning to creep its way up the trunk. "We must pull up that vine before it brings us harm," he told the others. "We cannot allow it to grow any higher."

"It is only a plant," said one of the younger geese. "It cannot hurt us."

"Let us destroy it now while it is weak and small," the old goose insisted. "It will be dangerous when it is big." The younger geese snickered at the foolishness of the old goose. He heard their comments and sighed sadly.

So the vine was allowed to creep up the tree. It grew thicker and stronger, winding itself round and round until it had reached the geese's home.

One morning, a trapper carrying a large net noticed the vine creeping up the tree trunk. It looked just like a ladder. The trapper lifted his eyes to the upper branches. When he saw the flock of geese, his heart leaped with hope.

Quietly and stealthily, the trapper climbed the vine. He spread out his net, and then he descended. By evening, every goose had gotten caught in the net.

"How did the trapper get up here?" they asked one another.

"It must have been that creeping vine!" replied one of them. Oh, if only they had listened to the wise old goose!

The younger geese now turned to the old one. He, too, had been caught. "Please forgive us," they pleaded. "We're so sorry that we doubted your wisdom. Please, tell us how to get out of this trap!"

The old goose remained silent, but his thoughts began to whirl. A plan came to him. He explained it to the other geese, and this time, they paid close attention.

At dawn, the trapper climbed the tree, expecting to find the geese struggling in his net. Instead, he found the birds lying stiffly, feet in the air. "They are all dead," he thought unhappily. "They must have been ill." Then he began plucking the geese out of the net and tossing them to the ground. When the last goose was dropped, all of the birds flapped their wings and flew off, safe and sound.

The trapper gazed at the flock, astonished. "These are the smartest geese I have ever seen!" he cried. Then he gathered up his net, climbed down the vine, and walked off, still shaking his head in amazement.

Identifying Author's Purpose

1. What is the author's purpose in paragraph 3?
   - Ⓐ to show that the younger geese do not share the old goose's concerns
   - Ⓑ to describe a creeping vine
   - Ⓒ to convince readers that the old goose is foolish
   - Ⓓ to make readers laugh at the younger geese's comments

Identifying Author's Purpose

2. The story was written mainly to
   - Ⓐ describe the foolishness of geese.
   - Ⓑ persuade readers to solve their own problems.
   - Ⓒ inform readers about one way to escape from a trap.
   - Ⓓ entertain readers with a story that teaches a lesson.

Interpreting Figurative Language

3. In paragraph 5, the writer compares the creeping vine to
   - Ⓐ a corkscrew.
   - Ⓑ a ladder.
   - Ⓒ a trap.
   - Ⓓ a rope.

Interpreting Figurative Language

4. The phrase *safe and sound* means
   - Ⓐ "protected from illness."
   - Ⓑ "free of all noise."
   - Ⓒ "able to hear well."
   - Ⓓ "unharmed in any way."

Summarizing

5. The story is mostly about
   - Ⓐ a flock of geese that narrowly escapes a trapper's net.
   - Ⓑ smart geese that think up a clever escape plan.
   - Ⓒ younger geese that learn from a wise old goose.
   - Ⓓ a creeping vine that becomes a great danger.

Summarizing

6. What is the best summary of the story?
   - Ⓐ A flock of geese refuses to see that a creeping vine is dangerous.
   - Ⓑ A flock of geese ignores a wise old goose's advice but finally listens when in danger.
   - Ⓒ A flock of smart geese fools a trapper by pretending to be dead.
   - Ⓓ A trapper climbs up a vine and traps some geese in his net, but they escape.

Read this newspaper article that was printed about Fire Safety Week. Then answer questions about the article. Choose the best answer for Numbers 7 through 12.

Be Smart, Be Safe

Fire Safety Week is approaching. The Billington Fire Department wants to remind our readers how important it is to have a smoke alarm in your home. A smoke alarm will warn you of the presence of smoke or a fire. The alarm makes a loud noise within seconds after smoke enters a room.

Firefighter Marla Rollins says that every home should have a working smoke alarm on each floor. "Additional smoke alarms should be placed just outside all bedrooms," says Rollins. "If your smoke alarms are battery operated, test them once a month. Replace dead batteries right away."

Rollins also states that most fires occur in the home. Leaving the kitchen while food is cooking is a major cause of home fires. Candles and electrical appliances also cause fires. "Never leave home with a candle burning or with an appliance left plugged in that's not meant to be plugged in all the time," says Rollins. "An ounce of prevention is worth a pound of cure."

"Fire drills are often done at school, but they are important exercises to do at home," reminds Rollins. "Fire drills teach people to exit their home safely and quickly if a fire breaks out. A good fire drill includes a plan for a central meeting place for all family members once they leave the house."

Rollins wants readers to know that they should always call the fire department before trying to put out a fire. When you spot a fire, leave the area immediately and call the fire department.

"This may sound like common sense," says Rollins, "but you wouldn't believe how often our warnings fall on deaf ears."

If a fire breaks out, Rollins suggests following these safety tips:

- Do not open a door if it feels hot. The fire on the other side may be burning fiercely. Seek another escape route or wait for help.

- Crawl on the floor when going through a smoky area.

- If your clothes catch on fire, stop where you are, drop to the ground, cover your face with your hands, and roll over and over to smother the flames.

- Once outside, don't return to the building. Call your fire department right away.

Identifying Author's Purpose

7. What is the author's purpose in the first paragraph?
   - (A) to tell people about Fire Safety Week
   - (B) to describe how smoke alarms work
   - (C) to persuade people to learn more about Fire Safety Week
   - (D) to inform people about the importance of smoke alarms

Identifying Author's Purpose

8. The article was written mainly to
   - (A) provide information about fire safety.
   - (B) tell where most fires occur.
   - (C) explain how to conduct a fire drill at home.
   - (D) persuade people to contact their fire departments for safety information.

Interpreting Figurative Language

9. Which of these best explains the phrase *an ounce of prevention is worth a pound of cure*?
   - (A) Cures for things that can be prevented are not always available.
   - (B) It is easier to prevent something bad than to deal with the results.
   - (C) It takes a lot of work to prevent something from happening, but the work is worth the effort.
   - (D) A cure is more valuable than prevention.

Interpreting Figurative Language

10. Words that fall on deaf ears are usually
    - (A) trusted.
    - (B) followed.
    - (C) ignored.
    - (D) doubted.

Summarizing

11. What is the main idea of the article?
    - (A) Most fires occur in the home.
    - (B) Only firefighters should attempt to put out a fire.
    - (C) People should learn how to protect themselves from fire.
    - (D) Smoke alarms should be in every home.

Summarizing

12. What is a good summary of the article?
    - (A) Knowing how to keep safe from fire can save people's lives.
    - (B) Fire Safety Week is the best time to learn how to keep safe from fire.
    - (C) Fire drills are important exercises to do at school and at home.
    - (D) Fire Safety Week is a good time to make sure the batteries in your smoke detectors are working.

Read this tall tale about a cowboy hero. Then answer questions about the tall tale. Choose the best answer for Numbers 1 through 12.

Pecos Bill was the greatest cowboy who ever lived. Before he came along, cowboys didn't know much about their job. They just rode around the cows, yelping and hollering. Pecos Bill taught the cowboys how to round up cattle and drive the herds. He also invented the six-shooter, the branding iron, and the lasso.

When Bill was a baby, his family lived in eastern Texas. One day, his father heard that another family was moving in about 50 miles away. Having neighbors that close was too crowded for him. So, he and his wife loaded their 18 kids and all of their belongings into a big, old covered wagon and headed farther west. Just as the wagon was about to cross the Pecos River, the rear left wheel hit a great rock. All at once, one-year-old Bill bounced out of the wagon. He landed so hard in the desert dirt that the wind got knocked out of him and he couldn't cry out. No one could have heard him anyway. His brothers and sisters were making such a racket in the back of the wagon that it wasn't possible even to hear thunder. It was evening before anyone noticed that the baby was missing. By then, it was too late to do anything about it.

As the wagon disappeared into the distance, young Bill lay there watching it. Suddenly, an old coyote walked over. He sniffed the little boy a few times. Then the coyote picked up the boy by the scruff of his neck and carried him to his den.

So it happened that Bill came to live with the coyotes. The coyotes taught the boy everything they knew about the wild out-of-doors. He was educated in the fine art of hunting and learned the proper way to howl at the moon. By the time he was 10, he could outrun and outhowl any coyote in the Southwest. The boy completely forgot what it was like to be human. Until he was 17, he believed that he was a full-blooded coyote.

Then, one day, a cowboy came riding through the desert and saw the boy roaming about on all fours. The cowboy told Bill that he wasn't a coyote; he was a human being. Bill growled at this news, but deep in his heart he knew the man was right. He'd always suspected that he was different from the other coyotes. So, Pecos Bill said good-bye to all of his four-legged friends and thanked them for all they had taught him. Then he rode off with the cowboy toward his ranch.

At first, acting like a human wasn't easy for Pecos Bill. But he soon got the hang of it. In no time, he became the roughest, toughest cowboy of them all.

Finding Main Idea

1. The tall tale is mostly about
   - Ⓐ the life of a cowboy.
   - Ⓑ Pecos Bill's days as a coyote.
   - Ⓒ the ways of the coyote.
   - Ⓓ Pecos Bill's adventures at a cattle ranch.

Recalling Facts and Details

2. How old was Bill when he lost his family?
   - Ⓐ 1
   - Ⓑ 4
   - Ⓒ 10
   - Ⓓ 17

Understanding Sequence

3. What was the first thing that happened after Bill fell out of the wagon?
   - Ⓐ An old coyote brought the boy to his den.
   - Ⓑ He watched the wagon disappear.
   - Ⓒ An old coyote walked over to him.
   - Ⓓ He landed hard in the desert dirt.

Recognizing Cause and Effect

4. Bill's family didn't look for him because
   - Ⓐ the coyote carried him off immediately.
   - Ⓑ his brothers and sisters were making too much noise.
   - Ⓒ they didn't realize that he was missing until it was too late.
   - Ⓓ no one could hear his cries when he fell out of the wagon.

Comparing and Contrasting

5. How was Pecos Bill different from other cowboys?
   - Ⓐ He used a lasso.
   - Ⓑ He came from eastern Texas.
   - Ⓒ He was rougher and tougher.
   - Ⓓ He was a full-blooded coyote.

Making Predictions

6. Predict what might have happened if Pecos Bill had not met the cowboy.
   - Ⓐ He would have still become a great cowboy.
   - Ⓑ He would have continued to live with the coyotes.
   - Ⓒ He would have left the coyotes anyway.
   - Ⓓ He would never have become a human being.

Finding Word Meaning in Context

7. In paragraph 3, *scruff* means
   - (A) "a scratch."
   - (B) "to shuffle along."
   - (C) "scent."
   - (D) "the back of the neck."

Identifying Author's Purpose

10. The author probably wrote the tall tale to
    - (A) describe the ways of the coyote.
    - (B) explain what a cowboy does.
    - (C) convince readers that Pecos Bill was the greatest cowboy who ever lived.
    - (D) entertain readers with a story about a cowboy hero.

Drawing Conclusions and Making Inferences

8. Bill probably got the name Pecos Bill because he
   - (A) was found by the cowboy near the Pecos River.
   - (B) was born near the Pecos River.
   - (C) was as swift as the Pecos River.
   - (D) asked the coyotes to name him after the Pecos River.

Interpreting Figurative Language

11. In the last paragraph, *got the hang of it* means
    - (A) "understood how something was hung."
    - (B) "learned how to do something."
    - (C) "spent time somewhere."
    - (D) "kept trying."

Distinguishing Between Fact and Opinion

9. Which of these is an *opinion*?
   - (A) Pecos Bill forgot what it was like to be human.
   - (B) Pecos Bill taught cowboys how to round up cattle.
   - (C) Pecos Bill was the greatest cowboy who ever lived.
   - (D) Pecos Bill was educated in the fine art of hunting.

Summarizing

12. What is the best summary of the tall tale?
    - (A) Pecos Bill was the greatest cowboy, and he taught the other cowboys everything they knew.
    - (B) Pecos Bill grew up to become the best coyote in the Southwest.
    - (C) Before he became the greatest cowboy, Pecos Bill grew up with the coyotes that saved him.
    - (D) Pecos Bill lived with the coyotes during his youth.

Read this article about the common cold. Then answer questions about the article. Choose the best answer for Numbers 13 through 24.

The common cold is the most widespread of all illnesses. It affects the nose, throat, and, sometimes, the air passages and lungs. The first symptoms of a cold are usually a tickle in the throat, a runny or stuffy nose, and sneezing. Other symptoms may develop, such as watering eyes, a low fever, a sore throat, and a cough. A cold sufferer may also experience aching muscles, headaches, and chills. Adults usually catch at least one cold each year. Most children get at least two or three colds a year.

Colds are most frequent during the winter months. This fact has led many people to believe that colds are caused by cold, wet conditions. The true cause, however, are viruses. Viruses are germs that are easily passed from one person to another. Cold viruses are spread when a person with a cold coughs or sneezes. People catch a cold by breathing in the tiny droplets of moisture that have been sprayed into the air. They can also get a cold by handling objects that carry cold germs.

One reason that colds are more common in winter is that people tend to spend more time indoors in cold weather. Being in close contact with people for long periods of time makes it easier for cold viruses to be passed on.

Unlike many other illnesses, a cold can strike a person more than once. The reason that a person can catch many colds is that there are more than 200 different cold viruses. A person's body can build up protection against a virus that has already attacked it. But this immunity cannot help a person fight off a different cold virus that strikes.

No one has found a cure for the common cold, but some people think that a cure is close at hand. Presently, there are plenty of cold medicines for sale in drugstores. But all of these medicines treat just symptoms. They can only relieve the discomfort a person with a cold suffers. Fortunately, most colds clear up within a week. Until then, people with colds should eat healthful foods and drink plenty of fluids.

People will try anything to prevent a cold. They may try to avoid cold drafts and dampness. Some may take large quantities of vitamin C. The best way to prevent a cold, however, is to stay away from people who have colds. That advice is cold comfort, though, for everyone who has to go to work and school.

Finding Main Idea

13. The best title for the article is
    - Ⓐ "How Viruses Spread."
    - Ⓑ "Health Myths."
    - Ⓒ "Treating Cold Symptoms."
    - Ⓓ "The Common Cold."

Recognizing Cause and Effect

16. Colds are more common in winter because
    - Ⓐ viruses can live only in cold weather.
    - Ⓑ people are more likely to be near others who have a cold.
    - Ⓒ people sneeze and cough more in cold weather.
    - Ⓓ cold viruses appear more often during cold months.

Recalling Facts and Details

14. How many colds do most children get each year?
    - Ⓐ at least one
    - Ⓑ one or two
    - Ⓒ two or three
    - Ⓓ three or more

Comparing and Contrasting

17. How is the common cold different from many other illnesses?
    - Ⓐ It can strike more than once.
    - Ⓑ It can strike only once.
    - Ⓒ It is caused by a virus.
    - Ⓓ It can be easily caught.

Understanding Sequence

15. Which of these cold symptoms appears first?
    - Ⓐ aching muscles
    - Ⓑ runny nose
    - Ⓒ cough
    - Ⓓ sore throat

Making Predictions

18. Predict how things would be different if there were a cure for the common cold.
    - Ⓐ No one would ever have a sore throat again.
    - Ⓑ Drugstores would go out of business.
    - Ⓒ People would spend more time outdoors.
    - Ⓓ People would miss fewer days of work and school each year.

Finding Word Meaning in Context

19. In paragraph 4, *immunity* means
    - (A) "a way to keep people with diseases away from healthy people."
    - (B) "the body's ability to fight off disease."
    - (C) "a drug given to people to protect them against disease."
    - (D) "the spread of a disease."

Identifying Author's Purpose

22. What was the author's main purpose for writing the article?
    - (A) to give information about the common cold
    - (B) to describe symptoms of the common cold
    - (C) to persuade readers to avoid people with colds
    - (D) to entertain readers with myths about the common cold

Drawing Conclusions and Making Inferences

20. From the article, you can tell that
    - (A) older people are more likely to catch a cold.
    - (B) people never catch colds in the summer.
    - (C) cold viruses spread more easily among children than adults.
    - (D) people can prevent colds by spending time outdoors.

Interpreting Figurative Language

23. In the last paragraph, what does *cold comfort* mean?
    - (A) "uninterested in relief"
    - (B) "comfortable despite cold temperatures"
    - (C) "something to help a sick person feel more comfortable"
    - (D) "no relief at all"

Distinguishing Between Fact and Opinion

21. Which of these is a *fact*?
    - (A) People will do anything to prevent a cold.
    - (B) The common cold is the most widespread of all illnesses.
    - (C) There is no illness worse than a cold.
    - (D) People with colds should be kind enough to avoid contact with others.

Summarizing

24. What is a good summary of the article?
    - (A) The common cold affects the nose, throat, and, sometimes, the air passages and lungs.
    - (B) The search for the cure for the common cold continues.
    - (C) The common cold is the most widespread of all illnesses, is caused by viruses, and has no cure.
    - (D) The most popular myth about the common cold is that it is caused by cold, wet conditions.

Read this biography of a great American. Then answer questions about the biography. Choose the best answer for Numbers 25 through 36.

He is one of the most respected men in United States history. He was a printer, a writer, a publisher, a scientist, an inventor, and a government leader. Who was this remarkable man? Benjamin Franklin, of course.

Benjamin Franklin was born on January 17, 1706, in Boston. He was the fifteenth of 17 children. Ben was a smart child, but his family was poor. At age 10, he had to leave school to help his father in his candle and soap shop. At age 12, Ben became an apprentice, or student worker, in a printing shop run by his half-brother James. Although Ben enjoyed his work, he did not like his older brother. So, at age 17, he ran away to Philadelphia. There he quickly found work as a printer.

Franklin was a hard worker. Within five years, he opened his own print shop. There he started his own newspaper and published *Poor Richard's Almanac*. This yearly calendar contained all kinds of facts, weather forecasts, and wise and witty sayings. Here are a few of Franklin's most famous sayings:

Early to bed and early to rise, makes a man healthy, wealthy, and wise.

An ounce of prevention is worth a pound of cure.

A penny saved is a penny earned.

As busy as he was with his printing business, Franklin also helped to make Philadelphia a better city. He set up the first lending library, the first fire department, and the first post office. He also helped establish a school that later became the University of Pennsylvania.

By age 42, Franklin's hard work and success had made him a rich man, so he retired and turned his attention to science. By sending up a kite during a storm, Franklin proved that lightning is a form of electricity. He had attached a key to the kite's string. When a lightning bolt struck the kite, the key became charged with electricity. Franklin then put his discovery to use by inventing the lightning rod. He also invented the Franklin stove, bifocal eyeglasses, and the glass harmonica.

Franklin is probably most remembered for his role in helping to build our nation. He was the first person to present the idea of uniting the 13 colonies. He spent 15 years in England trying to persuade the king to govern the colonies more fairly. In 1776, he signed the Declaration of Independence. During the Revolutionary War, he went to France and convinced the French to send troops and supplies to the colonists. He helped write the peace treaty that ended the war. He also helped to create the Constitution of the United States of America.

Benjamin Franklin lived long enough to see the Constitution become the basic law of the United States. He died on April 17, 1790, at age 84.

Finding Main Idea

25. What is the main idea of the biography?

ⓐ Ben Franklin lived long enough to see the birth of the United States of America.

ⓑ Ben Franklin was one of the most remarkable men in United States history.

ⓒ Ben Franklin was a hard worker.

ⓓ Ben Franklin was a poor boy who became a rich man.

Recalling Facts and Details

26. How many children were in Franklin's family?

ⓐ 12

ⓑ 15

ⓒ 16

ⓓ 17

Understanding Sequence

27. What happened immediately after Franklin went to Philadelphia?

ⓐ He became an apprentice in his half-brother's shop.

ⓑ He published *Poor Richard's Almanac.*

ⓒ He found work as a printer.

ⓓ He opened his own print shop.

Recognizing Cause and Effect

28. Franklin retired from printing at age 42 because

ⓐ he wanted to make Philadelphia a better city.

ⓑ he was rich and wanted to turn his attention to science.

ⓒ he wanted to prove that lightning is a form of electricity.

ⓓ he wanted to play a role in building our nation.

Comparing and Contrasting

29. How were the younger Ben Franklin and the older Ben Franklin alike?

ⓐ They both were hard workers who achieved a lot.

ⓑ They both wished they had more schooling.

ⓒ They were both interested in politics.

ⓓ They were both poor.

Making Predictions

30. What might have happened if Franklin had stayed in the printing business?

ⓐ He would never have become rich.

ⓑ He would not have had as much time for his interest in science.

ⓒ The Revolutionary War would have begun sooner.

ⓓ The Declaration of Independence would not exist.

Finding Word Meaning in Context

31. In paragraph 4, the word *establish* means
- Ⓐ "set up."
- Ⓑ "prove beyond a doubt."
- Ⓒ "try or attempt."
- Ⓓ "predict."

Identifying Author's Purpose

34. The biography was written mainly to
- Ⓐ tell readers about a great American.
- Ⓑ persuade readers to work as hard as Franklin.
- Ⓒ entertain readers with humorous stories about Franklin.
- Ⓓ describe the printing business in the 1700s.

Drawing Conclusions and Making Inferences

32. Readers of this biography can figure out that
- Ⓐ Franklin wanted to be president of the United States.
- Ⓑ Franklin was not a happy man.
- Ⓒ people thought that Franklin was a strange man.
- Ⓓ Franklin liked to explore new ideas and activities.

Interpreting Figurative Language

35. The saying *A penny saved is a penny earned* probably means that
- Ⓐ a person should save every penny that is earned.
- Ⓑ a person who does not work will never have any savings.
- Ⓒ money that is saved is money that is not wasted.
- Ⓓ one penny is not worth as much as two pennies.

Distinguishing Between Fact and Opinion

33. Which of these is an *opinion* about Ben Franklin?
- Ⓐ He was the first person to present the idea of uniting the 13 colonies.
- Ⓑ By age 42, he was a rich man.
- Ⓒ He was the most important founder of the United States.
- Ⓓ He proved that lightning is a form of electricity.

Summarizing

36. Which of these is the best summary of the biography?
- Ⓐ Ben Franklin was a poor boy who became a rich man.
- Ⓑ Ben Franklin was one of the greatest leaders in American history.
- Ⓒ Ben Franklin was a man who achieved much in his lifetime.
- Ⓓ Ben Franklin changed careers many times during his long life.

Read this story about a grandfather who enjoys sharing his memories. Then answer questions about the story. Choose the best answer for Numbers 37 through 48.

Changing Times

Last week, my family gathered for Thanksgiving dinner. My cousins and I were setting the table when our grandfather came in to help. Gramps loves to share stories of his childhood with us. My cousins and I enjoy asking him questions about what life was like when he was younger, even though some of the things Gramps says are hard to believe. My cousins and I think he likes to stretch the truth.

"Hey, Gramps," asked my cousin Jasmine, "what was your favorite fast food when you were growing up?"

"We didn't have fast food when I was growing up," he said. "All the food was slow."

"Come on, be serious. Where did you eat?" she asked.

"It was a place called home. My mother cooked every day, and when my father got home from work, we sat down together at the dining room table. And if I didn't like what she put on my plate, I had to sit there until I did like it. When I was done, I had to ask permission to leave the table."

"What about sports?" asked my cousin Micah. "Did you play soccer like us?"

"My parents never drove me to soccer practice, but that was because we had never heard of soccer. I got my exercise riding a bicycle that weighed more than I did."

"What were your favorite TV shows?" asked Rachel.

"We didn't have a television in our house until I was 11, but my grandparents had one. It was black and white, of course. There were only a few channels back then, and no one had ever heard of cable TV. Some people taped a plastic lens to the front of their TV to make the picture look larger.

"That's the silliest thing I've ever heard," remarked Jasmine.

"You think that's silly? Well, how about this," said Gramps. "I was 15 when I tasted my first pizza. We called it 'pizza pie,' and when I bit into it, I burned the roof of my mouth. Then the cheese slid off and stuck to my chin and burned that, too. And pizzas were not delivered to your home back then, but milk was."

"Milk? Why would people want milk brought to their home?" wondered Micah.

"What else were things like when you were a kid, Gramps?" I asked.

"My father bought our first car when I was 16. Before that, the only car in our family was my grandfather's Ford. He called it 'the tank' because he said it ran like the army tanks he drove in the war."

Gramps continued to reminisce about his childhood until the table was set and the turkey was ready to carve. As we sat and gave thanks, my cousins and I were grateful for our grandfather and all the stories he shares with us, even if we think they are tall tales.

Finding Main Idea

37. The first paragraph tells mainly about
- Ⓐ a family that gathers for a holiday meal.
- Ⓑ children who enjoy listening to their grandfather's stories.
- Ⓒ a man who likes to tell stories that are hard to believe.
- Ⓓ a man who remembers every detail of his childhood.

Recognizing Cause and Effect

40. If Gramps didn't like the food his mother put in front of him, he had to
- Ⓐ sit there until he did like it.
- Ⓑ ask permission to leave the table.
- Ⓒ help set the table the next time dinner was ready.
- Ⓓ promise to at least taste some of the food.

Recalling Fact and Details

38. Which of these is something Gramps didn't have until he was 15?
- Ⓐ a car
- Ⓑ a TV
- Ⓒ a pizza
- Ⓓ a bicycle

Comparing and Contrasting

41. What is one thing that Gramps did as a child that children today do?
- Ⓐ eat fast food
- Ⓑ play soccer
- Ⓒ ride a bike
- Ⓓ watch cable TV

Understanding Sequence

39. The boxes tell about some of the things that happened in the story.

Gramps helps his grandchildren set the table.		Gramps says that his parents never drove him to soccer practice.
1	**2**	**3**

Which of these belongs in box 2?
- Ⓐ Gramps talks about how he got his exercise.
- Ⓑ Gramps talks about his grandfather's car.
- Ⓒ Gramps tells the children about his first pizza pie.
- Ⓓ Gramps told the children that there was no fast food when he was young.

Making Predictions

42. Which of these is something the children would likely ask Gramps?
- Ⓐ "What was school like when you were young?"
- Ⓑ "Do you know what the weather will be like tomorrow?"
- Ⓒ "How often do you eat pizza now?"
- Ⓓ "Are you planning a vacation soon?"

Finding Word Meaning in Context

43. The best meaning for *reminisce* is

Ⓐ "remember something that had been forgotten."

Ⓑ "talk about events from the past."

Ⓒ "express unhappiness about something."

Ⓓ "read something aloud from memory."

Drawing Conclusions and Making Inferences

44. Readers of the story can figure out that

Ⓐ none of the things Gramps talked about actually happened.

Ⓑ Gramps regrets not being able to play soccer as a child.

Ⓒ Gramps is really telling the truth when he talks about his childhood.

Ⓓ Gramps thinks his grandchildren have an easier life than he had.

Distinguishing Between Fact and Opinion

45. Which statement tells an *opinion*?

Ⓐ "That's the silliest thing I've ever heard."

Ⓑ My cousins and I enjoy asking him questions about what life was like when he was a kid.

Ⓒ Last week, my family gathered for Thanksgiving dinner.

Ⓓ "He called it 'the tank' because he said it ran like the army tanks he drove in the war."

Identifying Author's Purpose

46. The story was written mainly to

Ⓐ get readers to learn more about their family members.

Ⓑ entertain readers with an enjoyable story.

Ⓒ explain how inventions have changed over the years.

Ⓓ describe what life was like long ago.

Interpreting Figurative Language

47. Someone who likes to *stretch the truth* is someone who likes to

Ⓐ lie.

Ⓑ pull the truth from people.

Ⓒ exaggerate.

Ⓓ imagine the future.

Summarizing

48. Which of these is the best summary of the story?

Ⓐ Grandchildren gather with their grandfather for Thanksgiving dinner.

Ⓑ Grandchildren enjoy hearing the stories of their grandfather's youth.

Ⓒ A grandfather makes up stories to entertain his grandchildren.

Ⓓ A grandfather tells his grandchildren about his life as a teenager.